Three Children's Novels by Christopher Pearse Cranch

Three Children's Novels by Christopher Pearse Cranch

The Last of the Huggermuggers: A Giant Story

Kobboltozo: A Sequel to The Last of the Huggermuggers

The Legend of Doctor Theophilus; or, The Enchanted Clothes

With Original Illustrations by the Author

EDITED, WITH AN INTRODUCTION, BY

Greta D. Little and Joel Myerson

The University of Georgia Press

Athens and London

Designed by Kathi L. Dailey
Set in Linotype Walbaum by Tseng Information Systems, Inc.
Printed and bound by Thomson-Shore, Inc.
The paper in this book meets the guidelines for
permanence and durability of the Committee on
Production Guidelines for Book Longevity of the
Council on Library Resources.

Printed in the United States of America

97 96 95 94 93 C 5 4 3 2 1

Library of Congress Cataloging in Publication Data

Cranch, Christopher Pearse, 1813–1892.
Three children's novels / Christopher Pearse Cranch ;
edited, with an introduction, by Greta D. Little and
Joel Myerson.
p. cm.
Includes bibliographical references.
Contents: The last of the Huggermuggers: a giant story—
Kobboltozo: a sequel to The last of the Huggermuggers—
The legend of Doctor Theophilus, or, The enchanted clothes.
ISBN 0–8203–1507–9 (alk. paper)
1. Children's stories, American. [1. Short stories.]
I. Little, Greta D. II. Myerson, Joel. III. Title.
PS1449.C8A6 1993
813′.3—dc20 92–24894
CIP
AC

British Library Cataloging in Publication Data available

FRONTISPIECE: *The Mer-King*, by Christopher Pearse Cranch.
From *Kobboltozo: A Sequel to The Last of the Huggermuggers*
(Boston: Phillips, Sampson, 1857).

Contents

Acknowledgments

We are grateful to Alan Brasher, Larry Carlson, Peter Drummey, Armida Gilbert, Alfred G. Litton, and Daniel Shealy for their help, and to Bert Dillon, chair of the English department at the University of South Carolina, for his support. Nancy Grayson Holmes has encouraged us at all stages of this project and we are in her debt.

Manuscript materials are quoted with the permission of the Andover-Harvard Theological School, Department of Rare Books, Cornell University Library, Houghton Library of Harvard University, and the Massachusetts Historical Society.

Introduction

Christopher Pearse Cranch's reputation has not fared well over the years. Henry James, who knew him, called Cranch a "painter, poet, musician, mild and melancholy humourist, [who] produced pictures the American traveller sometimes acquired and left verses that the American compiler sometimes includes."[1] And Perry Miller, in his anthology of *The Transcendentalists*, described Cranch as "one of the most futile and wasted talents" among the group.[2] If both James and Miller slight Cranch's work as a writer and artist, they both also ignore his contribution to children's literature. We hope that the republication of *The Last of the Huggermuggers* and *Kobboltozo: A Sequel to The Last of the Huggermuggers*, along with the first publication of *The Legend of Doctor Theophilus*, will help to bring Cranch and his writings for the young back into public view.

Cranch was unique among the Transcendentalists in that he was born a southerner, in Alexandria, then in the District of Columbia, on 8 March 1813.[3] His father was a judge who had married a niece of his lifelong friend John Quincy Adams, and Cranch counted Noah Webster among his uncles. With this background, it was natural for Cranch to look toward New England for his future after he was graduated from Columbian College (now George Washington University) in 1832.

Cranch attended the Harvard Divinity School, where he became friends with Theodore Parker, and, planning to become a minister, he went to Providence, Rhode Island, to preach after his graduation in 1835. He passed the winter in Andover, Maine, where he wrote his first extended literary work, "Childe Christopher," a poetic parody of "The Ancient Mariner" with himself as the title character.[4] The following summer he traveled to Illinois, and then on to Cincinnati, where his brother Edward had settled.

At Cincinnati, Cranch was given an opportunity to use and hone his literary talents when he was invited to join the staff of the *Western Messenger*, a journal devoted to spreading the word of Transcendentalism in the West. Cranch's work was appreciated, and when the *Messenger*'s editor, James Freeman Clarke, left Louisville for New England in the winter of 1837, Cranch moved to Louisville and edited the magazine. He substituted for Clarke again the following winter, and when Clarke returned in January 1839, he told Cranch the latest news from Boston, including the activities of Ralph Waldo Emerson, whose writings Cranch had read and praised in the pages of the *Messenger*.

Cranch's activities on behalf of the *Western Messenger* had whetted his literary appetite, and he became more and more attracted to Transcendentalism in general and Emerson in particular. Because Cranch had not been in any hurry to be ordained, it is fair to say that the ministry as a career held less interest for him as his literary activities and talents became more valued. In 1839 both of Cranch's talents came to the forefront. Cranch the artist began the "New Philosophy Scrapbook," containing caricatures of contemporaries, most notably those based on passages from Emerson's writings, the best known of which is the long-legged, barefoot, dinner-coat-clad transparent eyeball.[5] In that same year Cranch the writer composed one of his best poems, "Correspondences," which was deeply indebted to Emerson's ideas for its philosophical content.[6]

Cranch returned to New England in the fall of 1839. He visited his old Divinity School classmate Theodore Parker at West Roxbury, and Parker found him "full of spontaneous fellowship," though he recognized Cranch's dilettantish attitude would not make him "a man who the world will use well."[7] In December Cranch moved to Boston, where he attended a meeting of an informal group, the Transcendental Club, on the fifth. The meeting was held at the house of George Ripley, who would later organize the Brook Farm community, and among those present were the educator Bronson Alcott, the historian George Bancroft, the famous Unitarian divine William Ellery Channing, Emerson, the feminist Margaret Fuller, and Parker.[8] Of all this heady company, it was Emerson whose presence was most important to Cranch.

Cranch had followed Emerson's career with interest. He had read *Nature* soon after its publication in 1836, and had told his brother that it had sent him "athinking."[9] He had reviewed Emerson's address on "The American Scholar" in the *Messenger*, calling it "beautiful and masterly," and had privately described the Divinity School Address as "the utterance of a seer and a prophet, a word of profound truth."[10] Moreover, his cousin William Henry Furness was a childhood friend of Emerson's, and his brother John had met Emerson when both were in Rome in 1833.[11] And after arriving in Boston, Cranch attended Emerson's lecture series on "The Present Age," which he called "a treat whose worth I can find no words to express."[12]

On 2 March 1840, Cranch sent two of his poems to Emerson, "To the Aurora Borealis" and "Enosis," the latter having been written in Cranch's Boston hotel room while he was attending Emerson's lectures.[13] He asked Emerson to be the poems' "godfather" by placing them in the *Dial*, a new journal started by the Transcendentalists and edited by Margaret Fuller. And he expressed his "deep gratitude" for Emerson's ideas and his pleasure in Emerson's writings, concluding: "I utter no hollow compliments or vain imaginings when I say that I have owed to you more quickening influences & more elevating views in shaping my faith, than I can ever possibly express to you."[14] Emerson praised both poems to Fuller, and they appeared in the *Dial* for July 1840.[15]

Over the next few years, Cranch served as an itinerant preacher (but still put off his ordination), drew more caricatures of his contemporaries,[16] and contributed more poetry to the *Dial*. His closeness to Emerson and the Transcendentalists was simultaneously a boon to his poetry (he had a total of eighteen poems published in the *Dial*) and a curse to his ministry. John Quincy Adams heard Cranch preach in August 1840 and complained that he "gave out quite a stream of transcendentalism, quite unexpectedly."[17] The reformer Lydia Maria Child warned, after hearing Cranch preach a few months later, that he was "unconscious of the evil that lies under his very whiskers!"[18] By November 1840, Cranch wrote a friend that he had not had a paying preaching engagement for two months, for which he blamed the "sapient owls" of the Unitarian Association, who had "expunged" his name from "the list of *safe* men"; he had, he concluded, "the misfortune to have associated with Emerson, Ripley & those corrupters of youth, and have written for the Dial, and these are unpardonable offences."[19]

By 1842 Cranch had traveled to New York, where he met and fell in love with Elizabeth de Windt. He also became involved in the New York artistic scene, and particularly the Hudson River School of painters. He and Elizabeth were married in October 1843 and they settled in New York. Although his *Poems* (which was dedicated to Emerson) was published in May 1844, the book served almost as a postscript to his early poetic career. The move to New York and his new life as an artist both physically and aesthetically separated him from the Transcendentalists, and when he and Elizabeth embarked on a European tour in August 1846, Cranch put this part of his life behind him—the ministry for good, but the writing, as it turned out, only temporarily.[20]

The Cranches spent three years abroad, living for extended periods in Rome, Sorrento, and Florence, where they met and became friends of Elizabeth and Robert Browning. George William Cranch was born in March 1847 and Leonora Cranch was born in June 1848. Cranch continued his painting, but apparently earned only $2,000 for his work during this period. On this trip, as was true until the 1870s, the Cranches depended at least in part for their support on gifts from their fathers.[21]

The Cranches returned to New York in August 1849, living in the city but summering in places where Cranch could paint, such as the Catskills, the Berkshires, Niagara, and the Hudson. In the summer of 1852, they moved into the house at Lenox that the Hawthornes had vacated the previous fall. Caroline Amelia Cranch was born in May 1853. That October, the Cranches returned to Europe. It was there that Cranch met and began his lifelong friendship with James Russell Lowell. The next ten years were quiet ones, spent in Paris, with Cranch painting. A fourth and final child, Quincy Adams Cranch, was born in August 1855.

Upon their return to America in July 1863, the Cranches stayed in the New York City area, living at various times in the city, up the Hudson at Fishkill, or out on Staten Island. Cranch continued painting, and while his work was exhibited and sold, it did not fully support his family. Following the settlement of his father-in-law's estate after his death in 1870, Cranch achieved financial stability. No longer needing to maintain the pretense that his painting supported the family, he gradually began to leave that behind him as he returned to a literary career.

Cranch had never given up writing completely, publishing poetry and prose throughout the time he had concentrated on his painting. In 1872 he published his translation of the *Aeneid*, and the following year the family moved to Cambridge. There Cranch joined in the literary and social clubs of Boston and Cambridge, and saw other surviving friends from the Transcendentalist period. He published *Satan: A Libretto* in 1874 and *The Bird and the Bell, with Other Poems* the following year.

In 1880 the Cranches made their final trip to Europe, traveling there for two years. After returning to America, Cranch continued writing poetry, publishing his last book, *Ariel and Calaban*, in 1887. He died peacefully on 20 January 1892.

Cranch is today best known for his spirited caricatures of Emerson and other Transcendentalists. Like many people who have spread their abilities over a number of fields, Cranch failed to make a significant name for himself in any one of them. He himself was aware of this problem, and in the 1870s he expressed it in this fashion: "It is my misfortune (as regards worldly & pecuniary success) to have too many sides—to have been born (and educated) with a diversity of talents. . . . I have wooed too many mistresses; and the world punishes me for not shutting my eyes to all charmers but one."[22]

THE PUBLICATION OF *The Last of the Huggermuggers* and *Kobboltozo* came about as the result of a number of circumstances. After a downturn in his literary activities in the late 1840s, Cranch began to write more and more during the early 1850s. For two years he served as a correspondent for the *New York Evening Post*, but most of his work was poetry. As an expatriate writer—and a relatively unknown one at that—Cranch would have had little opportunity to publish his writings in America had he not had an agent or friend working for him abroad. That friend was George William Curtis, who had sailed to Europe with the Cranches in 1846. The friendship among the three was firm and lasting, and the Cranches named their firstborn after him. After his own return to America, Curtis had established himself as a best-selling popular author with such travel books as *Nile Notes of a Howadji* (1851), *Lotus-Eating, A Summer Book* (1852), and *Potiphar Papers* (1853). He also helped found *Putnam's Monthly Magazine* in 1853 and contributed the "Editor's Easy Chair" column to each issue of *Harper's Monthly Magazine* from 1854 to 1892. It was Curtis who used his connections with publishers on Cranch's behalf; as early as 1851 he had written his friend with this advice: "Keep on, and have a store of ammunition ready to let fly, and especially to send me everything you want to sell, and if I can not buy it, I can perhaps persuade others."[23]

Cranch availed himself of Curtis's assistance, and allowed him to place a number of his poems in New York and Boston periodicals. In the winter of 1854–1855, he wrote a children's book, which he described as "amusing, with some pathos at the end," drew illustrations on wood that could be used by an engraver, and sent everything to Curtis "to get a publisher for it."[24] Cranch had confidence in the book, since he had already tried it out on his children, eight-year-old Georgie and seven-year-old Leonora, with success. He told a friend that "the germ of it was conceived in inventing something to amuse" the children. Cranch read Georgie "the chapters as I wrote them, which amused and excited him, but always made him cry at the end over the sorrows of the poor giant."[25]

Curtis also liked the story, calling it "unique and droll," and he sent it to Appleton's. But their report, as he quoted it to Cranch in June, was a negative one: " 'We do not think that the story, although well written, would do to sell by itself. Fairy tales do not possess very great attractions to parents in search of books for their children, or if they do wish them, they more frequently look for a volume containing a variety, than for a single story.' " Curtis promised to continue seeking a publisher, vowing to send it to Ticknor and Fields, then if necessary to the Harpers.[26]

Other publishers must have agreed with Appleton's, for it was not until November that Curtis was able to report having success. The book had been accepted by the Boston firm of Phillips, Sampson, who were, coincidentally, the publishers of Emerson's *Representative Men* and *English Traits*. Curtis wrote that it was "to be done in the best and most costly manner." The publishers considered the sale "doubtful, (publishers always do)," but Curtis jocularly added "I don't believe you will make more than a million by it." He also enclosed a newspaper clipping with an advertisement for the book, described as intended "for large as well as small children," with illustrations "uncommonly spirited and beautiful."[27]

Unfortunately, the book was accepted and put into production too late to fully capitalize on the large volume of sales associated with the Christmas season, appearing as it did on 22 December.[28] His friend William Wetmore Story wrote to Cranch that "at 5 oclock of the day 'The Last of the Huggermuggers' was published, 300 copies were sold, & that Phillips & Sampson said that if the holiday had been a little farther off, they could easily have sold 10,000."[29] Cranch was delighted with this news, and he wrote James Russell Lowell of his anticipation at receiving a bound copy: "Huggermugger is coming—is coming to cheer our eyes—we shall see ourselves in print—clear large beautiful print, with our own illustrations engraved:—and across the great waters we hear the approving clapping of little hands and know that we are known among the juvenile gentry."[30]

Story, rather than Curtis,[31] was apparently the one who encouraged Cranch to write a sequel to *The Last of the Huggermuggers*, for in April 1856 he wrote Cranch that he had "promised on your behalf to Phillips, Sampson & Co. that you will write them another story with illustrations of about the length of 'Huggermugger,' and send it to them in July. So bestir your stumps." Still, as had often happened in Cranch's career, there were reservations about his work. Story reported that "your friends did not think it [*Huggermuggers*] up to your mark. We all know that you can do much better if you choose to put your energies to work; and now you must do so. You must invent a new story, and tell it in a livelier and sharper way."[32]

Cranch wrote *Kobboltozo: A Sequel to The Last of the Huggermuggers*, and that fall he reported to his brother Edward that it was "much better in subject, style, and in the designs." In fact, he went on, "Phillips & Sampson are much delighted with it, and say no expense will be spared to make it the most splendid book ever published in Boston," which news he found "pleasant and encouraging."[33] But to Lowell, Cranch complained, somewhat humorously, about the way in which books had to be fancified to ensure a good sale: "In what typographic dandyism and display will my bantling appear! P. & S. standing as godfather over it, decking it at the baptismal font with lace and gold and baubles—as if it were a Prince Imperial . . . But I dare say infantine America loves such things—the way gingerbread nowadays must be gilt—and every dog eared story book must blaze with illuminated letters—why dont they bind it in diamond-dusted and ruby spangled covers at once! The children of this generation go for *luxe (looks)* more than they did in our young days."[34]

Cranch, not wishing to lose sales again, sent in *Kobboltozo* early enough for it to appear in time for the Christmas season, and it was published on 10 December.[35] The book also appeared in time to be reviewed, although as a Christmas book aimed at a juvenile audience, it received short and general notices. Typical of the comments on *Kobboltozo* was the praise of it as "a very attractive and amusing book" in a two-sentence review in the *Boston Daily Advertiser*.[36] Reviewers had remembered *The Last of the Huggermuggers*, and the one in the *Boston Daily Evening Traveller* noted that everyone who read the first book will "rush to devour this one"; both were "capital stories, admirably illustrated."[37] And the reviewer in the *Boston Daily Evening Transcript* called Cranch's books "two sterling additions to the literature of childhood."[38]

Cranch's two children's books proved to be a financial windfall for him. *The Last of the Huggermuggers* sold "perhaps 12 to 1400 copies," even though it was published so late in the season,[39] and Cranch received a $500 payment through Lowell in late 1856.[40] At about the same time, Curtis sent Cranch another "$200 from Phillips, Sampson 'on account of Hugg. and Kobbo.'"[41] Ironically, Cranch earned at least as much from these two children's books as he had earned annually from his painting during his trip abroad in the 1840s.

THE SUCCESS OF *Kobboltozo*, which had been placed on sale early in the 1856 Christmas season, gave Cranch reason to hope for further success with his children's books. Curtis advised him to write more stories for the Christmas market: "Your name thus becomes associated with the holidays. Children will think of Santa Claus and

Cranch as brothers."[42] Cranch apparently took Curtis's advice, for in March 1857 he wrote to his longtime friend Mrs. Mary Preston Stearns of his plans for the next holiday season: "I have written a tale with an amusing shell and spiritual kernel with the motto 'For the young a story, for the old an allegory', which I am a good deal pleased with. I am preparing it and a fairy story for next Christmas."[43] The story he mentions must be *Doctor Theophilus*, which ends with "For the young, a magic-story. For the old, an allegory." "Burley-bones" is almost certainly the fairy story.

In July, Curtis conveyed the bad news that Phillips, Sampson would not be publishing a new Cranch story for Christmas. Cranch later explained to his brother that his work was "declined by the publisher on account of squally times beginning—and not for any fault of the stories."[44] Even without seeing them, Curtis offered to print the stories himself, "in my own 'Schoolfellow'—a magazine we publish for children, and a very popular affair for the young people."[45] However, the magazine ceased publication in 1857 without printing Cranch's stories. Curtis wrote in September that he had the manuscripts and blocks, which he would try to sell.[46]

The publishing market continued to struggle, and neither book was printed. Phillips, Sampson itself went bankrupt in 1859.[47] Consequently, Cranch's career as a storyteller gave way to his painting for the rest of his stay in Europe.

In 1863, when the Cranches returned to the United States, Cranch devoted more of his time to writing, especially poetry—some explicitly for children. His poems for children appeared in the leading children's periodicals of the time: *Riverside Magazine for Young People* and *St. Nicholas*. Many of these poems had been destined for a volume of children's poems to be called *Father Gander's Rhymes*, but no such collection ever appeared.

Cranch also began trying to publish his storybooks again. In 1866 he showed "Burley-bones" and the accompanying illustrations to Lowell, who wrote to Charles Eliot Norton that he hoped to get James T. Fields to publish the story.[48] Cranch wrote to Lowell in January 1867, asking him to inquire of Ticknor and Fields about the "Burley-bones" manuscript: "I fully understood that it was accepted, and would be published, sometime or another, in 'Our Young Folks'—But I am inclined to think that Fields intends to do nothing about it."[49] Cranch went on to mention that Henry Oscar Houghton (of the firm Hurd and Houghton) was thought to be looking for illustrated stories, and asked Lowell to show him "Burley-bones" and the illustrations for *Doctor Theophilus*.

In 1869 the two earlier books were reissued by Lee and Shepard, and Cranch suggested that Lowell approach them about the two manuscripts.[50] In May, he complained: "My unfortunate stories with the unfortunate blocks are I suppose still in limbo, in Boston. Mr. Woodman who undertook so enthusiastically to recommend them to Lee and Shepard has written no answer to a letter I sent him long ago. It's of no use I suppose writing again to him. They are doomed to be stillborn. . . . I can learn nothing about the other story and the illustrations—'Dr. Theophilus.' "[51]

The Theophilus manuscript continued to elude him. On 31 January 1870 he wrote Lowell:

> And will you just rummage once more in your drawers, for my missing Ms. 'Dr. Theophilus'—I can't help thinking

> it has slid into some chink, or been covered up out of sight, somewhere about your study.
>
> Mr. Fields, I am told, states that he knows nothing about the Ms.
>
> I am sorry to put you to this trouble. And if you shouldn't find it, the loss will not be irreparable—as I have a rough copy of the same—only the missing one is an improved edition.[52]

We cannot know whether Cranch ever found his manuscript; there is no evidence it was ever published. In any event, by the next year, Cranch had turned his attention to translating Virgil's *Aeneid.* Although his poems for young people continued to appear occasionally—the last in *St. Nicholas* for August 1891—he did not return to writing children's fiction. *The Last of the Huggermuggers* and *Kobboltozo* were reprinted several times in the nineteenth century, but after that 1870 letter, no further references concerning *Doctor Theophilus* or any other children's fiction have been found.

Although Cranch's fiction for children is better known, he also wrote a number of poems for young people as well. They appeared on the pages of *St. Nicholas, Hearth and Home*, and *Riverside Magazine for Young People* from 1869 until his death in 1892.

Many of these poems reveal the storytelling skill and sense of humor that characterized his two children's books. "The Painter's Scarecrow" tells of an independent young woman whose painting is repeatedly interrupted by rude, disruptive boys. Without a male protector and unable to find a policeman to help her, she creates a scarecrow to insure her privacy.[53] "A Chinese Story" tells of two near-sighted men who challenge one another to read the inscription on a distant marble tablet. Both men cheat, and their misdeeds are exposed when the tablet is replaced by a blank slab. The priest to whom they appeal for a judgment says:

> "I think, dear sirs, there must be few
> Blessed with such wondrous eyes as those you wear.
> There is no tablet with inscription there!
> There was one, it is true; 't was moved away,
> And yon plain tablet placed there yesterday."[54]

Cranch often wove lessons into the fabric of his poems and his fiction as well. "Burley Bones," the tale of a "big young fairy who had idle habits, and who got into difficulty" because he did not know the value of work, is the fairy story which Cranch originally prepared for Phillips, Sampson in 1857 and later believed to be accepted for publication in *Our Young Folks*.[55] An abridged version of the story appeared in *Hearth and Home* in 1871.[56] Burley Bones drinks punch and becomes drunk, embarrassing himself before Whirligig, the fairy maiden he wishes to woo. He is taken in by the kindly Deacon Hollyhock and his wife, Mrs. Pansy, but the ungrateful fairy repays their kindness by destroying their garden. Hollyhock takes him to the fairy court, and Burley Bones is sentenced to hard work in the garden for a year. He finally recognizes the error of his ways and becomes "quite a respectable and useful fairy." He is rewarded by a second encounter with Whirligig, who sees the remarkable change in him. They marry and live happily in the garden. Cranch uses his story-telling skills to teach a moral lesson: "And I conclude with the hope that all who read this may be as good and useful in their day and generation."

The fantasy which is characteristic of his fiction can also be found in his poetry. In "The Coal-Imp," when Cranch lights his fire, a spirit trapped in the coal appears. The artist captures his likeness on paper and asks how he got there. The spirit complains of his imprisonment and is released:

Then, taking the poker, I punched
  A hole in the half-burnt mass—
When the fire leaped up, and the Imp flew off
  In a laugh of flaming gas.[57]

In "How Willie Coasted by Moonlight," Willie is lured outside in the cold for an eerie ride with his "uncle" from Lapland. They go faster and faster down a hill with no end until they seem to be flying through the air and around the stars. A meteor flashes by knocking him off his seat and he wakes to find it was all a dream.[58]

Cranch's enjoyment of language play also shows up in his children's poetry. In "Four Charades" he composed four word puzzles for young readers. Each stanza suggests one syllable of the two-syllable words, and the third is a clue for the whole word.[59] The answers—*carpet, bargain, pic-nic,* and *nightmare*—were given in a later issue. "Phaeton" shows Cranch's penchant for wordplay as well as the interest in classical literature displayed in his poetry for adults. It is the story of the sun's charioteer, Phoebus Apollo, and his son, Phaeton.

> So, one day, Phaeton
> Said to his sire, "I'd like to drive your Sun—
> That is myself—dear sir, excuse the pun,—
> Twelve hours through space. You know you
> promised once
> Whatever I might ask." "I was a dunce,"
> Apollo said. "My foolish love for you,
> I fear, my son, that I shall sadly rue."

Pressing his case, Phaeton goes on,

> "Father, you swore it by the River Styx,—
> You know you did,—and you are in a fix."

Jupiter must save the earth from destruction by sending a thunderbolt to stop Phaeton's wild driving. Cranch interjects:

> (but wait—
> Here in parenthesis I'd like to state
> This may have been a *telegram;* for then
> Lightning dispatches were not known to men,
> But only used by heathen gods)[60]

Although Cranch had planned a volume of poetry for children, the project—like "Burley Bones" and *Doctor Theophilus*—never reached fruition. The book, the aborted *Father Gander's Rhymes*, included a number of fantasy poems featuring animal characters. Selections from the proposed book were eventually published in

Riverside Magazine for Young People with illustrations prepared by Cranch.[61]

CRANCH IS BEST remembered today for *The Last of the Huggermuggers* and *Kobboltozo*. His fantasy adventures for children hold a special place in the history of American children's books. For the practical-minded audience of nineteenth-century America, fantasy did not yet hold a major place. Hawthorne had introduced the notion of fairy tales in his *A Wonder Book* and *Tanglewood Tales*, but the fantastic adventure story was only beginning to emerge. Early publications for children were dominated by a concern for secular education in the works of Samuel Goodrich ("Peter Parley") and Jacob Abbott or religious education in the works published by the Sunday School Union and the American Tract Society. All these individuals and groups were opposed to fantasy stories or fairy tales that appealed to children's imaginations. Hawthorne and Cranch, however, had close ties to the Romantic movement in the United States and welcomed the added respect being granted to the imagination.

Cranch particularly was able to combine the genre of the fantasy tale represented by Hans Christian Andersen and the Brothers Grimm with the adventure story, especially the Robinsonades patterned after Defoe and Swift. In telling of a meeting between ordinary folk and make-believe giants and dwarfs, Cranch recalled the tradition of *Gulliver's Travels*, but added a new dimension to it. The stories are aggressively American, with only a subtle message about moral character woven into the plot.

The realistic and thoroughly practical Americans enter the

island world of fantasy—giants, dwarfs, witches, magic shellfish—and emerge unaffected. They retain control of themselves and of their lives. Readers are impressed by their ingenuity, not their piety or even by the power of supernatural forces. Although similar to the Robinsonade genre, *Huggermuggers* focuses more on the opportunistic ingenuity of Jacky Cable and Zebbedee Nabbum than on Cable's instinct for survival. Their plan to capture the giants and make them the main attraction of a P. T. Barnum show is born of self-interest, not self-revelation. Thus Cranch helped pave the way for pleasurable, non-instructive reading among young people.

The two stories also display his talent and affection for humorous wordplay. Cranch had fun using puns to name his characters: Mark Scrawler, the historian; Kobboltozo, the cobbler; Hammawhaxo, the carpenter; Stitchkin, the tailor. Nevertheless, his friends complained that the story was "too lachrymose" and urged him to write "in a livelier and sharper way."[62] Cranch himself thought the sequel "was much better in subject, style, and in the designs."[63]

Indeed, the plot of *Kobboltozo* is more cohesive and the theme more explicit. The focus has shifted from the adventurers to the dwarfs and their efforts to become giants themselves. The dwarfs are unable to grasp the message given them by the king of the sea:

> He that is a dwarf in spirit
> Never shall the isle inherit.
> Hearts that grow 'mid daily cares
> Grow to greatness unawares;
> Noble souls alone may know
> How the giants live and grow.

The dwarfs' refusal to work together tears their community apart and the Americans must teach the dwarfs how to live in harmony. In this story, Cranch is more direct in his use of physical size to represent moral character. He also reveals more clearly the mark of his Transcendentalist ties in the antimaterialistic message.

Although the advice of his friend arrived too late to have much impact on *Kobboltozo*, Cranch seems to have taken it to heart in writing *The Legend of Doctor Theophilus; or, The Enchanted Clothes*. Story had urged him: "Don't begin till you have settled all your plot in your mind; and if you can, let it hold a double story, an internal one and an external one, as Andersen's do, so that the wiseacres shall like it as well as the children. Read 'The Little Tin Soldier' of Andersen's, 'The Ugly Duckling,' 'The Emperor's New Clothes.' You *can* do this and you *must*."[64] The influence of Story's advice can be seen in the subtitle and further in the closing lines: "For the young, a magic-story. For the old, an allegory." The attention to clothes also reveals Cranch's interest in Thomas Carlyle and *Sartor Resartus*.

The opening chapter of *Doctor Theophilus* is reminiscent of Dickens's *Bleak House*, where the fog in Chancery Court represents the stagnation of the British legal system. However, Cranch's target is the medical profession in particular and reverence for the past in general. He uses puns to speak of Fogland's inhabitants as "Foggies or old (as we often spell the word) Fogies." Theophilus's foes are Dr. Sangsue (a leech), Dr. Musophof (hater of light), and Dr. Status-quo. His failure to heed the lesson of the encounter with his patient Godfrey shows the danger of the doctor's inaction. He is so wrapped up in his books and his work that he cannot see his peril. At last Theophilus discovers the enchanted clothes and does battle with the magician who made them, conquering him with one blow from the Bible.

Children will enjoy the doctor's cleverness in outsmarting his enemies as he destroys the Grand Panjandrum, and they will recognize the danger inherent in the good doctor's desire for fancy clothes. Children will immediately know that the energized clothes are magic, especially when the suit has tantrums. The news that his suit resembles the robes of the Grand Panjandrum will alert young readers that the magic clothes are dangerous. But the exact nature of that danger will be a surprise. Unlike the emperor's clothes, the doctor's clothes have too much substance. Instead of revealing the wearer's vanity, these clothes set out to ruin the good doctor and his reputation.

It is our hope that this book will introduce children, both young and old, to American fantasy in one of its early manifestations. Jacky Cable, Zebedee Nabbum, and the gentle giants have a place in American children's literature. Although overlooked, they helped define the genre in the new world, bringing brash American ways into the fantasy world of Huggermugger Island. Furthermore, this volume introduces the long-lost story of Dr. Theophilus and his nemesis, the enchanted clothes. The story-telling talents of Christopher Pearse Cranch have brought these characters to life with gentle humor and a now seldom-heard message of cooperation and harmony.

NOTES

1. Henry James, *William Wetmore Story and His Friends*, 2 vols. (Boston: Houghton Mifflin, 1903), 1:110.

2. *The Transcendentalists: An Anthology*, ed. Perry Miller (Cambridge: Harvard University Press, 1950), p. 179.

3. Biographical information is drawn from Leonora Cranch Scott, *The Life and Letters of Christopher Pearse Cranch* (Boston: Houghton Mifflin, 1917); F. DeWolfe Miller, "Christopher Pearse Cranch: New England Transcendentalist," Ph.D. dissertation, University of Virginia, 1942; F. DeWolfe Miller, *Christopher Pearse Cranch and His Caricatures of New England Transcendentalism* (Cambridge: Harvard University Press, 1951); Joel Myerson, *The New England Transcendentalists and the* Dial: *A History of the Magazine and Its Contributors* (Rutherford, N.J.: Fairleigh Dickinson University Press, 1980), pp. 133–39; and Robert D. Habich, *Transcendentalism and the* Western Messenger: *A History of the Magazine and Its Contributors, 1835–1841* (Rutherford, N.J.: Fairleigh Dickinson University Press, 1985). For a survey of the scholarship on Cranch, see David Robinson, "Christopher Pearse Cranch," in *The Transcendentalists: A Review of Research and Criticism*, ed. Joel Myerson (New York: Modern Language Association, 1984), pp. 123–30.

We are grateful to the Andover-Harvard Theological School, the Cornell University Library Department of Rare Books, the Houghton Library of Harvard University, and the Massachusetts Historical Society for permission to quote from materials in their possession.

4. The manuscript of this poem, at the University of Wyoming, shows it to be a decidedly juvenile effort. This was clearly Cranch's apprenticeship period: F. DeWolfe Miller describes the verses of this time as marked by "jejune religiosity," and even his friend John Sullivan Dwight called his

poetry "always beautiful, but feeble" (*Cranch*, p. 10; Dwight to Cranch, 12 August 1837, typescript copy, Massachusetts Historical Society).

5. Reproduced in Scott, *Cranch*, opposite p. 40, and Miller, *Cranch*, figure 3.

6. See Hazen C. Carpenter, "Emerson and Christopher Pearse Cranch," *New England Quarterly* 37 (March 1964): 18–42. "Correspondences" was published in the *Dial* 1 (January 1841): 381.

7. 12 October 1839, Parker, "Journal," 1:250, Andover-Harvard Theological School.

8. See Joel Myerson, "A Calendar of Transcendental Club Meetings," *American Literature* 44 (May 1972): 205.

9. Cranch to Edward Cranch, 22 December 1836, in Miller, "Cranch," p. 53.

10. "Emerson's Oration," *Western Messenger* 4 (October 1837): 184–89; entry of ca. 15 July 1838, "Manuscript Autobiography," in Miller, "Cranch," p. 81.

11. 5 April 1833, *The Journals and Miscellaneous Notebooks of Ralph Waldo Emerson*, ed. William H. Gilman, Ralph H. Orth, et al., 16 vols. (Cambridge: Harvard University Press, 1960–1982), 4:156.

12. Cranch to Julia Myers, 4 February 1840, in Scott, *Cranch*, p. 47.

13. "Enosis," which was influenced by Cranch's reading of *Nature*, appeared in the July 1840 *Dial* as "Stanzas." Its later title of "Gnosis" resulted from editors' misreadings of the German-style typography of its title in Cranch's *Poems* (see Miller, *Cranch*, p. 9; Miller, "Cranch," p. 105; Sidney E. Lind, "Christopher Pearse Cranch's 'Gnosis': An Error in Title," *Modern Language Notes* 62 [November 1947]: 486–88).

14. Cranch to Emerson, 2 March 1840, Collection of Joel Myerson.

15. See Emerson to Fuller, 3 March 1840, *The Letters of Ralph Waldo Emerson*, ed. Ralph L. Rusk and Eleanor M. Tilton, 8 vols. to date (New

York: Columbia University Press, 1939; 1990–), 2:258; Emerson to Cranch, 4 March 1840, *Letters*, 7:374.

16. One of the best that has survived shows a man lying on a couch, sipping wine while his wife glowers at him as she polishes his boots. A copy of the *Dial* is under the couch and the caption is a line from Caroline Sturgis's poem "Life": "Why for work art thou striving, / Why seeks't thou for aught? / To the soul that is living / All things shall be brought." See *Dial* 1 (October 1840): 195, for Sturgis's poem. The drawing is reproduced in both Scott, *Cranch*, opposite p. 60, and Miller, *Cranch*, figure 17.

17. *Memoirs of John Quincy Adams*, ed. Charles Francis Adams, 12 vols. (Philadelphia: J. B. Lippincott, 1874–1877), 10:345.

18. Child to Augusta King, 21 October 1840, Department of Rare Books, Cornell University Library.

19. Cranch to John Sullivan Dwight, 17 November 1840, in Myerson, "Transcendentalism and Unitarianism in 1840: A New Letter by C. P. Cranch," *CLA Journal* 16 (March 1973): 366–67.

20. A month before he left New York, Edgar Allan Poe portrayed Cranch in his "Literati of New York City" as "one of the least absurd contributors" to the *Dial*, who had since then "reformed his habits of thought and speech" (*Godey's Lady's Book* 33 [September 1846]: 18–19).

21. Elizabeth's father died in 1870, leaving them a sizable estate valued in 1890 at $54,000, with an annual interest of $3,600 (see Miller, *Cranch*, p. 17).

22. "The Book of Thoughts," commonplace book, 1872–1879, quoted in Francis B. Dedmond, "Christopher Pearse Cranch's 'Journal. 1839,' " in *Studies in the American Renaissance 1983*, ed. Joel Myerson (Charlottesville: University Press of Virginia, 1983), p. 149n.

23. George William Curtis to Cranch, 23 June 1851, typescript copy, Massachusetts Historical Society.

24. Cranch to Mary Preston Stearns, 10 August 1855, in Scott, *Cranch*, p. 215.

25. Cranch to George Luther Stearns, 25 December 1855, typescript copy, Massachusetts Historical Society.

26. George William Curtis to Cranch, 19 June 1855, typescript copy, Massachusetts Historical Society.

27. George William Curtis to Cranch, 21 November 1855, copy, Massachusetts Historical Society.

28. It was advertised as "nearly ready" in the 18 December *Boston Daily Evening Transcript*, and as published on that day in the 22 December *Boston Daily Advertiser.*

29. William Wetmore Story to Cranch, 24 December 1855, quoted in Cranch to James Russell Lowell, 27 January 1856, Houghton Library, Harvard University. In her transcript of Story's now-lost letter, Scott reports the sales as "nine hundred copies" (*Cranch*, p. 218).

30. Cranch to James Russell Lowell, 27 January 1856, Houghton Library, Harvard University.

31. Story wrote Cranch on 20 July 1856 that "I took upon myself to advise & direct as best I could for your advantage, although you had put the matter into George Curtis' hands, especially as he was at a distance and in love, 2 facts which interfere with business transactions" (typescript copy, Massachusetts Historical Society).

32. William Wetmore Story to Cranch, in Scott, *Cranch*, pp. 220–21.

33. Cranch to Edward Cranch, 14 September 1856, in Scott, *Cranch*, pp. 222–23. Story also found the book good, writing to Cranch that it was "a great step in advance of 'Huggermugger' " (20 July 1856, typescript copy, Massachusetts Historical Society).

34. Cranch to James Russell Lowell, [Fall? 1856?], Houghton Library, Harvard University.

35. *Boston Daily Advertiser*, 10 December 1856, p. 2.

36. *Boston Daily Advertiser*, 12 December 1856, p. 2.

37. *Boston Daily Evening Traveller*, 16 December 1856, p. 4.

38. "Knick," "Juvenile Books and Periodicals," *Boston Daily Evening Transcript*, 20 December 1856, p. 1.

39. George William Curtis to Cranch, 28 December 1856, typescript copy, Massachusetts Historical Society.

40. Lowell had written Cranch in August about sending him $500 from "my Boston publishers," but he had not received it by November. But a letter from John Sullivan Dwight the next month reports that "Lowell tells me they have just sent you solid cash" (Cranch to James Russell Lowell, 24 November 1856, Houghton Library, Harvard University; Dwight to Cranch, 7 December 1856, typescript copy, Massachusetts Historical Society).

41. George William Curtis to Cranch, 28 December 1856, typescript copy, Massachusetts Historical Society.

42. George William Curtis to Cranch, 28 December 1856, in Scott, *Cranch*, p. 228.

43. Cranch to Mary Preston Stearns, 30 March 1857, typescript copy, Massachusetts Historical Society. Mrs. Stearns, the wife of antislavery crusader Major George Luther Stearns, met Cranch through Frederic Henry Hedge when the latter was pastor of a Unitarian church in Bangor, Maine, in 1836–1837. They became lifelong friends.

44. Cranch to Edward Cranch, 12 November 1857, in Miller, "Cranch," p. 290.

45. George William Curtis to Cranch, 18 July 1857, typescript copy, Massachusetts Historical Society.

46. George William Curtis to Cranch, 14 September 1857, typescript copy, Massachusetts Historical Society.

47. The firm suspended business in September 1859, within a month after the deaths of both partners, Moses D. Phillips and Charles Sampson (see Emerson, *Letters*, 5:172n).

48. James Russell Lowell to Charles Eliot Norton, 30 May 1866, in Miller, "Cranch," p. 309.

49. Cranch to James Russell Lowell, 28 January 1867, Houghton Library, Harvard University.

50. Cranch to James Russell Lowell, 16 December 1868, Houghton Library, Harvard University.

51. Cranch to James Russell Lowell, 10 May 1869, Houghton Library, Harvard University.

52. Cranch to James Russell Lowell, 31 January 1870, Houghton Library, Harvard University.

53. *St. Nicholas* 5 (September 1878): 714–15.

54. Originally published in *Lippincott's Magazine of Popular Literature and Science* 11 (April 1873): 398–99, this poem was plagiarized and appeared under the name of W. J. Bahmer in *St. Nicholas* 15 (September 1888): 839.

55. Cranch mentioned the fairy story in a letter to Mary Preston Stearns, 30 March 1857, and again in a letter to James Russell Lowell, 28 January 1867 (see above).

56. Scott cites a description of the old de Windt home, which she claims is the opening of the fairy story "Burley-bones" (see *Cranch*, p. 203). Nothing resembling this passage occurs anywhere in the text published in *Hearth and Home*.

57. *St. Nicholas* 2 (February 1875): 220–21.

58. *St. Nicholas* 3 (January 1876): 168–70.

59. *St. Nicholas* 5 (April 1878): 406.

60. *St. Nicholas* 11 (February 1884): 288–90.

61. Four installments of Father Gander's rhymes, including a preface and some ten poems, appeared in *Riverside Magazine for Young People* 4 (1870): 60, 117, 152, 360. That number is about half of the twenty poems Miller indicates were originally planned ("Cranch," p. 320).

62. William Wetmore Story to Cranch, 18 April 1856, in Scott, *Cranch*, pp. 220–21.

63. Cranch to Edward Cranch, 14 September 1856, in Scott, *Cranch*, p. 223.

64. William Wetmore Story to Cranch, 18 April 1856, in Scott, *Cranch*, p. 221.

Note on the Texts

Even though Phillips, Sampson went bankrupt in 1859, both *The Last of the Huggermuggers* and *Kobboltozo* remained in print into the next century. The Boston firm of Mayhew and Baker reprinted both books in 1860 as a single volume with the title of *Giant Hunting; or, Little Jacket's Adventures.* In 1889 each book was reprinted separately in the *Little Jacket Series* by the Boston firm of Lee and Shepard.[1] The New York reprint firm of A. L. Burt combined both books under the title of *The Last of the Huggermuggers* in a new edition in 1901, with illustrations by J. Watson Davis. It was sold as part of the *St. Nicholas Series for Boys and Girls*, and was advertised for sale as late as 1912. Cranch did not make changes in any of these texts.

The Last of the Huggermuggers: A Giant Story (Boston: Phillips, Sampson, 1856) and *Kobboltozo: A Sequel to The Last of the Huggermuggers* (Boston: Phillips, Sampson, 1857) are reprinted from the first editions.[2] We have corrected obvious typographical errors and normalized illustrated letters in some chapter openings; nothing else has been changed in the written text. However, we have been unable to reproduce all of Cranch's illustrations; samples from these are included in the present edition.

The history of *The Legend of Doctor Theophilus* is more complicated. The manuscript dropped from sight by 1870. It was not in the possession of Cranch's descendants when Leonora Cranch Scott wrote her life of her father in 1917, nor when F. DeWolfe Miller gained access to the Cranch family manuscripts in the 1940s when writing his doctoral dissertation.[3] It was not in the collections of materials presented by Cranch's descendants to the Massachusetts Historical Society or the University of Wyoming. The manuscript finally surfaced in the 1980s, when it was sold to Goodspeed's bookstore in Boston.[4]

Doctor Theophilus is written in ink on both sides of nineteen leaves of paper and contains cancellations and additions in Cranch's hand. A cover sheet has the notation "Revised Edition," making it possible for the manuscript to be either the "improved edition" Cranch sent to Lowell or the "rough copy of the same" (i.e., with cancellations and additions present) that Cranch had kept after making a clean copy to send to Lowell (see Cranch's letter of 31 January 1870, quoted above). The text for *Doctor Theophilus* in the present volume is a conservatively emended edition of the final level of text in the manuscript: that is, the layer of text which omits Cranch's deletions and incorporates his additions. Under normal circumstances, this final level of text would either have been the basis for a fair copy made for the printer or would have itself served as setting copy for the printer; in both cases, such formal matters as spelling, punctuation, and paragraphing would have been normalized. Therefore, in editing the present text, we have made the following silent emendations: corrected spellings that could not be verified in contemporary dictionaries, normalized punctuation (particularly commas in series) according to Cranch's general practice in the manuscript, regularized paragraphing, and added or deleted words for clarity of expression. Our intention has been to present a text as close as possible to the revised manuscript text, while at the same time incorporating the "tidying-up" changes that authors expected as part of the publication process. Our text, then, presents the final level of text in Cranch's manuscript as it would have been prepared for publication, according to contemporary standards, by a copyeditor or typesetter.

NOTES

1. Mayhew and Baker used the Phillips, Sampson plates in their reprinting, as did Lee and Shepard.

2. Both books used for printer's copy in the present edition are from the H. Bradley Martin Collection and are now in the Collection of Joel Myerson.

3. See Scott, *The Life and Letters of Christopher Pearse Cranch* (Boston: Houghton Mifflin, 1917), and F. DeWolfe Miller, "Christopher Pearse Cranch: New England Transcendentalist," Ph.D. dissertation, University of Virginia, 1942.

4. The manuscript of *Doctor Theophilus* was part of a collection that included Cranch's correspondence with Ralph Waldo Emerson. Emerson's letters to Cranch were sold separately by Goodspeed's; the other manuscripts, including *Doctor Theophilus*, are in the Collection of Joel Myerson.

The Last of the Huggermuggers: A Giant Story

1

How Little Jacket would go to Sea

I dare say there are not many of my young readers who have heard about Jacky Cable, the sailor-boy, and of his wonderful adventures on Huggermugger's Island. Jacky was a smart Yankee lad, and was always remarkable for his dislike of staying at home, and a love of lounging upon the wharves, where the sailors used to tell him stories about sea-life. Jacky was always a little fellow. The country people, who did not much like the sea, or encourage Jacky's fondness for it, used to say, that he took so much salt air and tar smoke into his lungs that it stopped his growth. The boys used to call him Little Jacket. Jacky, however, though small in size, was big in wit, being an uncommonly smart lad, though he did play truant sometimes, and seldom knew well his school-lessons. But some boys learn faster out of school than in school, and this was the case with Little Jacket. Before he was ten years old, he knew every rope in a ship, and could manage a sail-boat or a row-boat with equal ease. In fine, salt water seemed to be his element; and he was never so happy or so wide awake as when he was lounging with the sailors in the docks. The neighbors thought he was a sort of good-for-nothing, idle boy, and his parents often grieved that he was not fonder of home and of school. But Little Jacket was not a bad boy, and was really learning a good deal in his way, though he did not learn it all out of books.

Well, it went on so, and Little Jacket grew fonder and fonder of the sea, and pined more and more to enlist as a sailor, and go off to the strange countries in one of the splendid big ships. He did not say much about it to his parents, but they saw what his longing was, and after thinking and talking the matter over together, they concluded that it was about as well to let the boy have his way.

So when Little Jacket was about fifteen years old, one bright summer's day, he kissed his father and mother, and brothers and sisters, and went off as a sailor in a ship bound to the East Indies.

2

His Good and his Bad Luck at Sea

It was a long voyage, and there was plenty of hard work for Little Jacket, but he found several good fellows among the sailors, and was so quick, so bright, so ready to turn his hand to every thing, and withal of so kind and social a disposition, that he soon became a favorite with the Captain and mates, as with all the sailors. They had fine weather, only too fine, the Captain said, for it was summer time, and the sea was often as smooth as glass. There were lazy times then for the sailors, when there was little work to do, and many a story was told among them as they lay in the warm moonlight nights on the forecastle. But now and then there came a blow of wind, and all hands had to be stirring—running up the shrouds, taking in sails, pulling at ropes, plying the pump; and there was many a hearty laugh among them at the ducking some poor fellow would get, as now and then a wave broke over the deck.

Things went on, however, pretty smoothly with Little Jacket, on the whole, for some time. They doubled the Cape of Good Hope, and were making their way as fast as they could to the coast of Java, when the sky suddenly darkened, and there came on a terrible storm. They took in all the sails they could, after having several carried away by the wind. The vessel scudded, at last, almost under bare poles. The storm was so violent as to render her almost unmanageable, and they were carried a long way out of their course. Everybody had tremendous work to perform, and Little Jacket began to wish he were safe on dry land again. Day after day the poor vessel drifted and rolled. The sky was so dark, that the Captain could not take an observation to tell in what part of the ocean they were. At last, they saw that they were driving towards some enormous cliffs that loomed up in the darkness. Every one lost hope of the ship being saved. Still they neared the cliffs, and now they saw the white breakers ahead, close under them. The Captain got the boats out, to be in readiness for the worst. But the sea was too rough to use them. At last, with a mighty crash, the great ship struck upon the black rocks. All was confusion and wild rushing of the salt waves over them, and poor Jacky found himself in the foaming surge. Struggling to reach the shore, a great wave did what he could not have done himself. He was thrown dripping wet, and bruised, upon the rocks. When he came to himself, he discovered that several of his companions had also reached the shore, but nothing more was seen of the ship. She had gone down in the fearful tempest, and carried I know not how many poor fellows down with her.

3

How he fared on Shore

All this was bad enough, as Little Jacket thought. But he was very thankful that he was alive and on shore, and able to use his limbs, and that he found some companions still left. He was not long either in using his wits, and in making the best use of the chances still left him. He found himself upon a rocky promontory. But on climbing a little higher up, he could see that there was beyond it, and joining on to it, a beautiful smooth beach. The rocks were enormous, and he and his comrades had hard work to clamber over them. It took them a good while to do so, exhausted as they were by fatigue, and dripping with wet. At length they reached the beach, the sands of which were of very large grain, and so loose that they had to wade nearly knee deep through them. The country back of the shore seemed very rocky and rough, and here and there were trees of an enormous magnitude. Every thing seemed on a gigantic scale, even to the weeds and grasses that grew on the edge of the beach, where it sloped up to join the main land. And they could see, by mounting on a stone, the same great gloomy cliffs which they saw before the ship struck, but some miles inland. But what most attracted their attention, was the enormous and beautiful great sea-shells, which lay far up on the shore. They were not only of the most lovely colors, but quite various in form, and so large that a man might creep into them. Little Jacket was not long in discovering the advantage of this fact, for they might be obliged, when night came on, to retire into these shells, as they saw no house anywhere within sight. Now, Little Jacket had read Robinson Crusoe, and Gulliver's Travels, and had half believed the wonderful stories of Brobdingnag; but he never thought that he should ever be actually wrecked on a giant's island. There now seemed to be a probability that it might be so, after all. What meant these enormous weeds, and trees, and rocks, and grains of sand, and these huge shells? What meant these great cliffs in the distance? He began to feel a little afraid. But he thought about Gulliver, and how well he fared after all, and, on the whole, looked forward rather with pleasure at the prospect of some strange adventure. Now and then he thought he could make out something like huge footprints on the shore—but this might be fancy. At any rate, they would hide themselves if they saw the giant coming. And if they could only find some food to live upon, they might get on tolerably well for a time. And perhaps this was only a fancy about giants, and they might yet find civilized beings like themselves living here.

Now Little Jacket began to be very hungry, and so did his companions—there were six of them—and they all determined to look about as far inland as they dared to go, for some kind of fruit or vegetable which might satisfy their appetites. They were not long in discovering a kind of beach-plum, about as big as watermelons, which grew on a bush so tall, that they had to reach the fruit at arm's length, and on tiptoe. The stalks were covered with very sharp thorns, about a foot long. Some of these thorns they cut off, (they had their knives in their pockets still,) for Little Jacket thought they might be of service to them in defending themselves against any wild animal which might prowl around at night. It chanced that Little Jacket found good use for his in the end, as we shall see. When they had gathered enough of these great plums, they sat down and dined upon them. They found them a rather coarse, but not unpalatable fruit. As they were still very wet, they took off their clothes, and dried them in the sun; for the storm had ceased, and the sun now came out very warm. The great waves, however, still dashed up on the beach. When their clothes were dry, they put them on, and feeling a good deal refreshed, spent the rest of the day in looking about to see what was to be done for the future. As night came on, they felt a good deal dispirited; but Little Jacket encouraged his companions, by telling stories of sailors who had been saved, or had been taken under the protection of the kings of the country, and had married the kings' daughters, and all that. So they found a group of the great shells near each other, seven of them, lying high and dry out of the reach of the dashing waves, and, after bidding each other good night, they crept in. Little Jacket found his dry and clean, and having curled himself up, in spite of his anxiety about the future, was soon fast asleep.

4

How Huggermugger came along

Now it happened that Little Jacket was not altogether wrong in his fancies about giants, for there *was* a giant living in this island where the poor sailors were wrecked. His name was Huggermugger, and he and his giantess wife lived at the foot of the great cliffs they had seen in the distance. Huggermugger was something of a farmer, something of a hunter, and something of a fisherman. Now, it being a warm, clear, moonlight night, and Huggermugger being disposed to roam about, thought he would take a walk down to the beach to see if the late storm had washed up any clams* or oysters, or other shell-fish, of which he was very fond. Having gathered a good basket full, he was about returning, when his eye fell upon the group of great shells in which Little Jacket and his friends were reposing, all sound asleep.

"Now," thought Huggermugger, "my wife has often asked me to fetch home one of these big shells. She thinks it would look pretty on her mantel-piece, with sunflowers sticking in it. Now I may as well gratify her, though I can't exactly see the use of a shell without

*The "clam" is an American bivalve shell-fish, so called from hiding itself in the sand. A "clam chowder" is a very savory kind of thick soup, of which the clam is a chief ingredient. I put in this note for the benefit of little English boys and girls, if it should chance that this story should find its way to their country.

a fish in it. Mrs. Huggermugger must see something in these shells that I don't."

So he didn't stop to choose, but picked up the first one that came to his hand, and put it in his basket. It was the very one in which Little Jacket was asleep. The little sailor slept too soundly to know that he was travelling, free of expense, across the country at a railroad speed, in a carriage made of a giant's fish-basket. Huggermugger reached his house, mounted his huge stairs, set down his basket, and placed the big shell on the mantel-piece.

"Wife," says he, "here's one of those good-for-nothing big shells you have often asked me to bring home."

"Oh, what a beauty," says she, as she stuck a sunflower in it, and stood gazing at it in mute admiration. But, Huggermugger being hungry, would not allow her to stand idle.

"Come," says he, "let's have some of these beautiful clams cooked for supper—they are worth all your fine shells with nothing in them."

So they sat down, and cooked and ate their supper, and then went to bed.

Little Jacket, all this time, heard nothing of their great rumbling voices, being in as sound a sleep as he ever enjoyed in his life. He awoke early in the morning, and crept out of his shell—but he could hardly believe his eyes, and thought himself still dreaming, when he found himself and his shell on a very high, broad shelf, in a room bigger than any church he ever saw. He fairly shook and trembled in his shoes, when the truth came upon him that he had been trapped by a giant, and was here a prisoner in his castle. He had time enough, however, to become cool and collected, for there was not a sound to be heard, except now and then something resembling a thunder-like snoring, as from some distant room. "Aha," thought Little Jacket to himself, "it is yet very early, and the giant is asleep, and there may be time yet to get myself out of his clutches."

He was a brave little fellow, as well as a true Yankee in his smartness and ingenuity. So he took a careful observation of the room, and its contents. The first thing to be done was to let himself down from the mantel-piece. This was not an easy matter, as it was very high. If he jumped, he would certainly break his legs. He was not long in discovering one of Huggermugger's fishing-lines tied up and lying not far from him. This he unrolled, and having fastened one end of it to a nail which he managed just to reach, he let the other end drop (it was as large as a small rope) and easily let himself down to the floor. He then made for the door, but that was fastened. Jacky, however, was determined to see what could be done, so he pulled out his jackknife, and commenced cutting into the corner of the door at the bottom, where it was a good deal worn, as if it had been gnawed by the rats. He thought that by cutting a little now and then, and hiding himself when the giant should make his appearance, in time he might make an opening large enough for him to squeeze himself through. Now Huggermugger was by this time awake, and heard the noise which Jacky made with his knife.

"Wife," says he, waking her up—she was dreaming about her beautiful shell—"wife, there are those eternal rats again, gnawing, gnawing at that door; we must set the trap for them to-night."

Little Jacket heard the giant's great voice, and was very much astonished that he spoke English. He thought that giants spoke nothing but "chow-chow-whangalorum-hallaballoo with a-ruffle-bull-bagger!" This made him hope that Huggermugger would not eat him. So he grew very hopeful, and determined to persevere. He kept at his work, but as softly as he could. But Huggermugger heard the noise again, or fancied he heard it, and this time came to see if he could not kill the rat that gnawed so steadily and so fearlessly. Little Jacket heard him coming, and rushed to hide himself. The nearest place of retreat was one of the giant's great boots, which lay on the floor, opening like a cave before him. Into this he rushed. He had hardly got into it before Huggermugger entered.

5

What happened to Little Jacket in the Giant's Boot

Huggermugger made a great noise in entering, and ran up immediately to the door at which Little Jacket had been cutting, and threshed about him with a great stick, right and left. He then went about the room, grumbling and swearing, and poking into all the corners and holes in search of the rat; for he saw that the hole under the door had been enlarged, and he was sure that the rats had done it. So he went peeping and poking about, making Little Jacket not a little troubled, for he expected every moment that he would pick up the boot in which he was concealed, and shake him out of his hiding-place. Singularly enough, however, the giant never thought of looking into his own boots, and very soon he went back to his chamber to dress himself. Little Jacket now ventured to peep out of the boot, and stood considering what was next to be done. He hardly dared to go again to the door, for Huggermugger was now dressed, and his wife too, for he heard their voices in the next room, where they seemed to be preparing their breakfast. Little Jacket now was puzzling his wits to think what he should do, if the giant should take a fancy to put his boots on before he could discover another hiding-place. He noticed, however, that there were other boots and shoes near by, and so there was a chance that Huggermugger might choose to put on some other pair. If this should be the case, he might lie concealed where he was during the day, and at night work away again at the hole in the door, which he hoped to enlarge enough soon, to enable him to escape. He had not much time, however, for thought; for the giant and his wife soon came in. By peeping out a little, he could just see their great feet shuffling over the wide floor.

"And now, wife," says Huggermugger, "bring me my boots." He was a lazy giant, and his wife spoiled him, by waiting on him too much.

"Which boots, my dear," says she.

"Why, the long ones," says he; "I am going a hunting to-day, and shall have to cross the marshes."

Little Jacket hoped the long boots were not those in one of which he was concealed, but unfortunately they were the very ones. So he felt a great hand clutch up the boots, and him with them, and put them down in another place. Huggermugger then took up one of the boots and drew it on, with a great grunt. He now proceeded to take up the other. Little Jacket's first impulse was to run out and throw himself on the giant's mercy, but he feared lest he should be taken for a rat. Besides he now thought of a way to defend himself, at least for a while. So he drew from his belt one of the long thorns he had cut from the bush by the seaside, and held it ready to thrust it into his adversary's foot, if he could. But he forgot that though it was as a sword in *his* hand, it was but a thorn to a giant. Huggermugger had drawn the boot nearly on, and Little Jacket's daylight was all gone, and the giant's great toes were pressing down on him, when he gave them as fierce a thrust as he could with his thorn.

"Ugh!" roared out the giant, in a voice like fifty mad bulls; "wife, wife, I say!"

"What's the matter, dear?" says wife.

"Here's one of your confounded needles in my boot. I wish to gracious you'd be more careful how you leave them about!"

"A needle in your boot?" said the giantess, "how can that be? I haven't been near your boots with my needles."

"Well, you feel there yourself, careless woman, and you'll see."

Whereupon the giantess took the boot, and put her great hand down into the toe of it, when Little Jacket gave another thrust with his weapon.

"O-o-o-o!!" screams the wife. "There's something here, for it ran into my finger; we must try to get it out." She then put her hand in again, but very cautiously, and Little Jacket gave it another stab, which made her cry out more loudly than before. Then Huggermugger put his hand in, and again he roared out as he felt the sharp prick of the thorn.

"It's no use," says he, flinging down the boot in a passion, almost breaking Little Jacket's bones, as it fell. "Wife, take that boot to the cobbler, and tell him to take that sharp thing out, whatever it is, and send it back to me in an hour, for I must go a hunting to-day."

So off the obedient wife trotted to the shoemaker's, with the boot under her arm. Little Jacket was curious to see whether the shoemaker was a giant too. So when the boot was left in his workshop, he contrived to peep out a little, and saw, instead of another Huggermugger, only a crooked little dwarf, not more than two or three times bigger than himself. He went by the name of Kobboltozo.

"Tell your husband," says he, "that I will look into his boot presently—I am busy just at this moment—and will bring it myself to his house."

Little Jacket was quite relieved to feel that he was safe out of the giant's house, and that the giantess had gone. "Now," thought he, "I think I know what to do."

After a while, Kobboltozo took up the boot and put his hand down into it slowly and cautiously. But Little Jacket resolved to keep quiet this time. The dwarf felt around so carefully, for fear of having his finger pricked, and his hand was so small in comparison with that of the giant's, that Little Jacket had time to dodge around his fingers and down into the toe of the boot, so that Kobboltozo could feel nothing there. He concluded, therefore, that whatever it was that hurt the giant and his wife, whether needle, or pin, or tack, or thorn, it must have dropped out on the way to his shop. So he laid the boot down, and went for his coat and hat. Little Jacket knew that now was his only chance of escape—he dreaded being carried back to Huggermugger—so he resolved to make a bold move. No sooner was the dwarf's back turned, as he went to reach down his coat, than Little Jacket rushed out of the boot, made a spring from the table on which it lay, reached the floor, and made his way as fast as he could to a great pile of old boots and shoes that lay in a corner of the room, where he was soon hidden safe from any present chance of detection.

6

How Little Jacket escaped from Kobboltozo's Shop

Great was Huggermugger's astonishment, and his wife's, when they found that the shoemaker told them the truth, and that there was nothing in the boot which could in any way interfere with the entrance of Mr. Huggermugger's toes. For a whole month and a day, it puzzled him to know what it could have been that pricked him so sharply.

Leaving the giant and his wife to their wonderment, let us return to Little Jacket. As soon as he found the dwarf was gone, and that all was quiet, he came out from under the pile of old shoes, and looked around to see how he should get out. The door was shut, and locked on the outside, for Kobboltozo had no wife to look after the shop while he was out. The window was shut too, the only window in the shop. This window, however, not being fastened on the outside, the little sailor thought he might be able to open it by perseverance. It was very high, so he pushed along a chair towards a table, on which he succeeded in mounting, and from the table, with a stick which he found in the room, he could turn the bolt which fastened the window inside. This, to his great joy, he succeeded in doing, and in pulling open the casement. He could now, with ease, step upon the window sill. The thing was now to let himself down on the other side. By good luck, he discovered a large piece of leather on the table. This he took and cut into strips, and tying them together, fastened one end to a nail inside, and boldly swung himself down in sailor fashion, as he had done at the giant's, and reached the ground. Then looking around, and seeing nobody near, he ran off as fast as his legs could carry him. But alas! he knew not where he was. If he could but find a road which would lead him back to the seaside where his companions were, how happy would he have been! He saw nothing around him but huge rocks and trees, with here and there an enormous fence or stone wall. Under these fences, and through the openings in the stone walls he crept, but could find no road. He wandered on for some time, clambering over great rocks and wading through long grasses, and began to be very tired and very hungry; for he had not eaten any thing since the evening before, when he feasted on the huge beach plums. He soon found himself in a sort of blackberry pasture, where the berries were as big as apples; and having eaten some of these, he sat down to consider what was to be done. He felt that he was all alone in a great wilderness, and out of which he feared he never could free himself. Poor Jacky felt lonely and sad enough, and almost wished he had discovered himself to the dwarf, for whatever could have happened to him, it could not have been worse than to be left to perish in a wilderness alone.

7

How he made use of Huggermugger in Travelling

While Little Jacket sat pondering over his situation, he heard voices not far off, as of two persons talking. But they were great voices, as of trumpets and drums. He looked over the top of the rock against which he was seated, and saw for the first time the entire forms of Huggermugger and his wife, looming up like two great lighthouses. He knew it must be they, for he recognized their voices. They were standing on the other side of a huge stone wall. It was the giant's garden.

"Wife," said Huggermugger, "I think now I've got my long boots on again, and my toe feels so much better, I shall go through the marsh yonder and kill a few frogs for your dinner; after that, perhaps I may go down again to the seashore, and get some more of those delicious clams I found last night."

"Well, husband," says the wife, "you may go if you choose for your clams, but be sure you get me some frogs, for you know how fond I am of them."

So Huggermugger took his basket and his big stick, and strode off to the marsh. "Now," thought the little sailor, "is my time. I must watch which way he goes, and if I can manage not to be seen, and can only keep up with him—for he goes at a tremendous pace—we shall see!"

So the giant went to the marsh, in the middle of which was a pond, while Little Jacket followed him as near as he dared to go. Pretty soon, he saw the huge fellow laying about him with his big stick, and making a great splashing in the water. It was evident he was killing Mrs. Huggermugger's frogs, a few of which he put in his basket, and then strode away in another direction. Little Jacket now made the best use of his little legs that ever he made in his life. If he could only keep the giant in sight! He was much encouraged by perceiving that Huggermugger, who, as I said before, was a lazy giant, walked at a leisurely pace, and occasionally stopped to pick the berries that grew everywhere in the fields. Little Jacket could see his large figure towering up some miles ahead. Another fortunate circumstance, too, was, that the giant was smoking his pipe as he went, and even when Little Jacket almost lost sight of him, he could guess where he was from the clouds of smoke floating in the air, like the vapor from a high-pressure Mississippi steamboat. So the little sailor toiled along, scrambling over rocks, and through high weeds and grass and bushes, till they came to a road. Then Jacky's spirits began to rise, and he kept along as cautiously, yet as fast as he could, stopping only when the giant stopped. At last, after miles and miles of walking, he caught a glimpse of the sea through the huge trees that skirted the road. How his heart bounded! "I shall at least see my messmates again," he said, "and if we are destined to remain long in this island, we will at least help each other, and bear our hard lot together."

It was not long before he saw the beach, and the huge Huggermugger groping in the wet sand for his shell-fish. "If I can but reach my companions without being seen, tell them my strange adventures, and all hide ourselves till the giant is out of reach, I shall be only too happy." Very soon he saw the group of beautiful great shells, just as they were when he left them, except that *his* shell, of course, was not there, as it graced Mrs. Huggermugger's domestic fire-side. When he came near enough, he called some of his comrades by name, not too loud, for fear of being heard by the shell-fish-loving giant. They knew his voice, and one after another looked out of his shell. They had already seen the giant, as they were out looking for their lost companion, and had fled to hide themselves in their shells.

"For heaven's sake," cried the little sailor, "Tom, Charley, all of you! don't stay here; the giant will come and carry you all off to his house under the cliffs; his wife has a particular liking for those beautiful houses of yours. I have just escaped, almost by miracle. Come, come with me—here—under the rocks—in this cave—quick, before he sees us!"

So Little Jacket hurried his friends into a hole in the rocks, where the giant would never think of prying. Huggermugger did not see them. They were safe. As soon as he had filled his basket, he went off, and left nothing but his footprints and the smoke of his pipe behind him.

After all, I don't think the giant would have hurt them, had he seen them. For he would have known the difference between a sailor and a shell-fish at once, and was no doubt too good-natured to injure them, if they made it clear to his mind that they were not by any means fish; but, on the contrary, might disagree dreadfully with his digestion, should he attempt to swallow them.

8

How Little Jacket and his Friends left the Giant's Island

Very soon the sailors found a nice, large, dry cave in the rocks. There they brought dry sea-weed and made it into beds, and lived on the fish and fruits, which they had not much difficulty in obtaining. They even dragged their beautiful shells into the cave, and made little closets and cupboards of them. Their cups and plates were made of smaller bivalve shells. Their drink was clear spring-water, which they discovered near by, mixed with the juice of fruits.

They lived in this way for several weeks, always hoping some good luck would happen. At last, one day, they saw a ship a few miles from the shore. They all ran to the top of a rock, and shouted and waved their hats. Soon, to their indescribable joy, they saw a boat approaching the shore. They did not wait for it to reach the land, but being all good swimmers, with one accord plunged into the sea and swam to the boat. The sailors in the boat proved to be all Americans, and the ship was the Nancy Johnson, from Portsmouth, N.H., bound to the East Indies, but being out of water had made for land to obtain a supply.

The poor fellows were glad enough to get on board ship again. As they sailed off, they fancied they saw in the twilight, the huge forms of the great Mr. and Mrs. Huggermugger on the rocks, gazing after them with open eyes and mouths. They pointed them out to the people of the ship, as Little Jacket related his wonderful adventures; but the sailors only laughed at them, and saw nothing but huge rocks and trees; and they whispered among themselves, that the poor fellows had lived too long on tough clams and sour berries, and cold water, and that a little jolly life on board ship would soon cure their disordered imaginations.

A PEEP AT THE HUGGERMUGGERS.

THE GIANT PICKS UP LITTLE JACKET'S BEDROOM.

MRS. HUGGERMUGGER ADMIRES THE SHELL AND SUNFLOWER.

THE SHOEMAKER AT WORK.

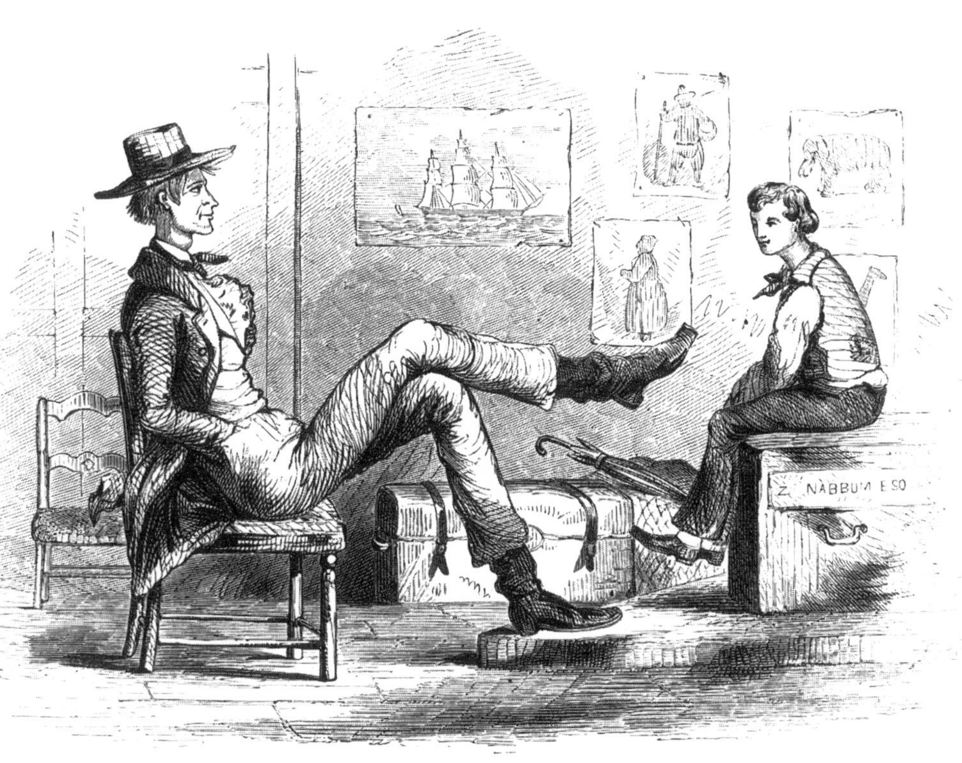

MR. NABBUM HEARS LITTLE JACKET'S STORY.

A NEW MODE OF CONVEYANCE.

9

Mr. Nabbum

Little Jacket and his friends were treated very kindly by the Captain and crew of the Nancy Johnson, and as a few more sailors were wanted on board, their services were gladly accepted. They all arrived safely at Java, where the ship took in a cargo of coffee. Little Jacket often related his adventures in the giant's island, but the sailors, though many of them were inclined to believe in marvellous stories, evidently did not give much credit to Jacky's strange tale, but thought he must have dreamed it all.

There was, however, one man who came frequently on board the ship while at Java, who seemed not altogether incredulous. He was a tall, powerful Yankee, who went by the name of Zebedee Nabbum. He had been employed as an agent of Barnum, to sail to the Indies and other countries in search of elephants, rhinoceroses, lions, tigers, baboons, and any wild animals he might chance to ensnare. He had been fitted out with a large ship and crew, and all the men and implements necessary for this exciting and dangerous task, and had been successful in entrapping two young elephants, a giraffe, a lion, sixteen monkeys, and a great number of parrots. He was now at Java superintending the manufacture of a very powerful net of grass-ropes, an invention of his own, with which he hoped to catch a good many more wild animals, and return to America, and make his fortune by exhibiting them for Mr. Barnum.

Now Zebedee Nabbum listened with profound attention to Little Jacket's story, and pondered and pondered over it.

"And after all," he said to himself, "why shouldn't it be true? Don't we read in Scripter that there war giants once? Then why hadn't there ought to be some of 'em left—in some of them remote islands whar nobody never was? Grimminy! If it should be true—if we should find Jacky's island—if we should see the big critter alive, or his wife—if we could slip a noose under his legs and throw him down—or carry along the great net and trap him while he war down on the beach arter his clams, and manage to tie him and carry him off in my ship! He'd kick, I know. He'd a kind o' roar and struggle, and maybe swamp the biggest raft we could make to fetch him. But couldn't we starve him into submission? Or, if we gave him plenty of clams, couldn't we keep him quiet? Or couldn't we give the critter *Rum*?—I guess he don't know nothin' of ardent sperets—and obfusticate his wits—and get him reglar boozy—couldn't we do any thing we chose to, then? An't it worth tryin', any how? If we *could* catch him, and get him to Ameriky alive, or only his skeleton, my fortune's made, I cal'late. I kind o' can't think that young fellow's been a gullin' me. He talks as though he'd seen the awful big critters with his own eyes. So do the other six fellows—they couldn't all of 'em have been dreamin'."

So Zebedee had a conversation one day with the Captain of the Nancy Johnson, and found out from him that he had taken the latitude and longitude of the coast where they took away the shipwrecked sailors. The Captain also described to Zebedee the appearance of the coast; and, in short, Zebedee contrived to get all the information about the place the Captain could give him, without letting it appear that he had any other motive in asking questions than mere curiosity.

10

Zebedee and Jacky put their heads together

Zebedee now communicated to Little Jacket his plans about sailing for the giant's coast, and entrapping Huggermugger and carrying him to America. Little Jacket was rather astonished at the bold scheme of the Yankee, and tried to dissuade him from attempting it. But Zebedee had got his head so full of the notion now, that he was determined to carry out his project, if he could. He even tried to persuade Little Jacket to go with him, and his six companions, and finally succeeded. The six other sailors, however, swore that nothing would tempt them to expose themselves again on shore to the danger of being taken by the giant. Little Jacket agreed to land with Zebedee and share all danger with him, on condition that Zebedee would give him half the profits Barnum should allow them from the exhibition of the giant in America. But Little Jacket made Zebedee promise that he would be guided by his advice, in their endeavors to ensnare the giant. Indeed, a new idea had entered Jacky's head as to the best way of getting Huggermugger into their power, and that was to try persuasion rather than stratagem or force. I will tell you the reasons he had for so thinking.

1. The Huggermuggers were not Ogres or Cannibals. They lived on fish, frogs, fruit, vegetables, grains, &c.

2. The Huggermuggers wore clothes, lived in houses, and were surrounded with various indications of civilization. They were not savages.

3. The Huggermuggers spoke English, with a strange accent, to be sure. They seemed sometimes to prefer it to their own language. They must, then, have been on friendly terms with English or Americans, at some period of their lives.

4. The Huggermuggers were not wicked and blood-thirsty. How different from the monsters one reads about in children's books! On the contrary, though they had little quarrels together now and then, they did not bite nor scratch, but seemed to live together as peaceably and lovingly, on the whole, as most married couples. And the only time he had a full view of their faces, Little Jacket saw in them an expression which was really good and benevolent.

All these facts came much more forcibly to Jacky's mind, now that the first terror was over, and calm, sober reason had taken the place of vague fear.

He, therefore, told Mr. Nabbum, at length, his reasons for proposing, and even urging, that unless Huggermugger should exhibit a very different side to his character from that which he had seen, nothing like force or stratagem should be resorted to.

"For," said Little Jacket, "even if you succeeded, Mr. Nabbum, in throwing your net over his head, or your noose round his leg, as you would round an elephant's, you should consider how powerful and intelligent, and, if incensed, how furious an adversary you have to deal with. None but a man out of his wits would think of carrying him off to your ship by main force. And as to your idea of making him drunk, and taking him aboard in that condition, there is no knowing whether drink would not render him quite furious, and ten times more unmanageable than ever. No, take my word for it, Mr. Nabbum, that I know Huggermugger too well to attempt any of your tricks with him. You cannot catch him as you would an elephant or a hippopotamus. Be guided by me, and see if my plan don't succeed better than yours."

"Well," answered Zebedee, "I guess, arter all, Jacky, you may be right. You've seen the big varmint, and feel a kind o' acquainted with him, so you see I won't insist on my plan, if you've any better. Now, what I want to know is, what's your idee of comin' it over the critter?"

"You leave that to me," said Little Jacket; "if talking and making friends with him can do any thing, I think I can do it. We may coax him away; tell him stories about our country, and what fun he'd have among the people so much smaller than himself, and how they'd all look up to him as the greatest man they ever had, which will be true, you know; and that perhaps the Americans will make him General Huggermugger, or His Excellency President Huggermugger; and you add a word about our nice oysters, and clam-chowders.

"I think there'd be room for him in your big ship. It's warm weather, and he could lie on deck, you know; and we could cover him up at night with matting and old sails; and he'd be so tickled at the idea of going to sea, and seeing strange countries, and we'd show him such whales and porpoises, and tell him such good stories, that I think he'd keep pretty quiet till we reached America. To be sure, it's a long voyage, and we'd have to lay in an awful sight of provisions, for he's a great feeder; but we can touch at different ports as we go along, and replenish our stock.

"One difficulty will be, how to persuade him to leave his wife—for there wouldn't be room for two of them. We must think the matter over, and it will be time enough to decide what to do when we get there. Even if we find it impossible to get him to go with us, we'll get somebody to write his history, and an account of our adventures, and make a book that will sell."

11

They sail for Huggermugger's Island

So Little Jacket sailed with Mr. Zebedee Nabbum, in search of the giant's island. They took along a good crew, several bold elephant-hunters, an author to write their adventures, an artist to sketch the Huggermuggers, Little Jacket's six comrades, grappling-irons, nets, ropes, harpoons, cutlasses, pistols, guns, the two young elephants, the lion, the giraffe, the monkeys, and the parrots.

They had some difficulty in finding the island, but by taking repeated observations, they at last discovered land that they thought must be it. They came near, and were satisfied that they were not deceived. There were the huge black cliffs—there were the rocky promontory—the beach. It was growing dusk, however, and they determined to cast anchor, and wait till morning before they sent ashore a boat.

Was it fancy or not, that Little Jacket thought he could see in the gathering darkness, a dim, towering shape, moving along like a pillar of cloud, now and then stooping to pick up something on the shore—till it stopped, and seemed looking in the direction of the ship, and then suddenly darted off towards the cliffs, and disappeared in the dark woods.

12

The Huggermuggers in a new light

I think the giant must have seen the ship, and ran home at full speed to tell his wife about it. For in the morning early, as Little Jacket and Nabbum and several others of the boldest of the crew had just landed their boat, and were walking on the beach, whom should they see but Huggermugger and his wife hastening towards them with rapid strides. Their first impulse was to rush and hide themselves, but the Huggermuggers came too fast towards them to allow them to do so. There was nothing else to do but face the danger, if danger there was. What was their surprise to find that the giant and giantess wore the most beaming smiles on their broad faces. They stooped down and patted their heads with their huge hands, and called them, in broken English, "pretty little dolls and dears, and where did they come from, and how long it was since they had seen any little men like them—and wouldn't they go home and see them in their big house under the cliffs?" Mrs. Huggermugger, especially, was charmed with them, and would have taken them home in her arms— "she had no children of her own, and they should live with her and be her little babies." The sailors did not exactly like the idea of being treated like babies, but they were so astonished and delighted to find the giants in such good humor, that they were ready to submit to all the good woman's caresses.

Little Jacket then told them where they came from, and related his whole story of having been shipwrecked there, and all his other adventures. As he told them how Huggermugger had carried home the big shell with him in it, sound asleep; how he had let himself down from the mantel-piece, and had tried to escape by cutting at the door; and how, when he heard Huggermugger coming, he had rushed into the boot, and how he had pricked the giant's toe when he attempted to draw his boot on, and how the boot and he were taken to the cobbler's—then Huggermugger and his wife could contain themselves no longer, but burst into such peals of laughter, that the people in the ship, who were watching their movements on shore through their spy-glasses, and expected every moment to see their companions all eaten alive or carried off to be killed, knew not what to make of it. Huggermugger and his wife laughed till the tears ran down their faces, and made such a noise in their merriment, that the sailors wished they were further off. They, however, were in as great glee as the giant and giantess, and began to entertain such a good opinion of them, that they were ready to assent to any thing the Huggermuggers proposed. In fact, except in matter of size, they could see very little difference between the giants and themselves. All Zebedee Nabbum's warlike and elephant-trapping schemes melted away entirely, and he even began to have a sort of conscientious scruple against enticing away the big fellow who proved to be such a jolly good-humored giant. He was prepared for resistance. He would have even liked the fun of throwing a noose over his head, and pulling him down and harpooning him, but this good-humored, merry laughter, this motherly caressing, was too much for Zebedee. He was overcome. Even Little Jacket was astonished. The once dreaded giant was in all respects like them—only O, so much bigger!

So, after a good deal of friendly talk, Huggermugger invited the whole boat's crew to go home with him to dinner, and even to spend some days with him, if they would. Little Jacket liked the proposal, but Zebedee said they must first send back a message to the ship, to say where they were going. Huggermugger sent his card by the boat, to the rest of the ship's company—it was a huge piece of pasteboard, as big as a dining-table—saying, that he and Mrs. H. would be happy, some other day, to see all who would do him the honor of a visit. He would come himself and fetch them in his fish-basket, as the road was rough, and difficult for such little folks to travel.

13

Huggermugger Hall

The next morning Huggermugger appeared on the beach with his big basket, and took away about half a dozen of the sailors. Zebedee and Little Jacket went with them. It was a curious journey, jogging along in his basket, and hanging at such a height from the ground. Zebedee could not help thinking what a capital thing it would be in America to have a few big men like him to lift heavy stones for building, or to carry the mail bags from city to city, at a railroad speed. But, as to travelling in his fish-basket, he certainly preferred our old-fashioned railroad cars.

They were all entertained very hospitably at Huggermugger Hall. They had a good dinner of fish, frogs, fruit, and vegetables, and drank a kind of beer, made of berries, out of Mrs. Huggermugger's thimble, much to the amusement of all. Mrs. Huggermugger showed them her beautiful shell, and made Little Jacket tell how he had crept out of it, and let himself down by the fishing-line. And Huggermugger made him act over again the scene of hiding in the boot. At which all laughed again. The little people declined their hosts' pressing invitation to stay all night, so Huggermugger took them all back to their boat. They had enough to tell on board ship about their visit. The next day, and the day after, others of the crew were entertained in the same way at Huggermugger Hall, till all had satisfied their curiosity. The giant and his wife being alone in the island, they felt that it was pleasant to have their solitude broken by the arrival of the little men. There were several dwarfs living here and there in the island, who worked for the giants, of whom Kobboltozo was one; but there were no other giants. The Huggermuggers were the last of their race. Their history, however, was a secret they kept to themselves. Whether they or their ancestors came from Brobdignag, or whether they were descended from Gog and Magog, or Goliath of Gath, they never would declare.

Mr. Scrawler, the author, who accompanied the ship, was very curious to know something of their history and origin. He ascertained that they learned English of a party of adventurers who once landed on their shore, many years before, and that the Huggermugger race had long inhabited the island. But he could learn nothing of their origin. They looked very serious whenever this subject was mentioned. There was evidently a mystery about them, which they had particular reasons never to unfold. On all other subjects they were free and communicative. On this, they kept the strictest and most guarded silence.

14

Kobboltozo astonishes Mr. Scrawler

Now it chanced that some of the dwarfs I have spoken of, were not on the best of terms with the Huggermuggers. Kobboltozo was one of these. And the only reason why he disliked them, as far as could be discovered, was, that they were giants, and he (though a good deal larger than an ordinary sized man) was but a dwarf. He could never be as big as they were. He was like the frog that envied the ox, and his envy and hatred sometimes swelled him almost to bursting. All the favors that the Huggermuggers heaped upon him, had no effect in softening him. He would have been glad at almost any misfortune that could happen to them.

Now Kobboltozo was at the giant's house one day when Mr. Scrawler was asking questions of Huggermugger about his origin, and observed his disappointment at not being furnished with all the information he was so eager to obtain; for Mr. Scrawler calculated to make a book about the Huggermuggers and all their ancestors, which would sell. So while Mr. Scrawler was taking a stroll in the garden, Kobboltozo came up to him and told him he had something important to communicate to him. They then retired behind some shrubbery, where Kobboltozo, taking a seat under the shade of a cabbage, and requesting Mr. Scrawler to do the same, looked around cautiously, and spoke as follows:—

"I perceive that you are very eager to know something about the Huggermuggers' origin and history. I think that I am almost the only one in this island, besides them, who can gratify your curiosity in this matter. But you must solemnly promise to tell no one, least of all the giants, in what way you came to know what I am going to tell you, unless it be after you have left the island, for I dread Huggermugger's vengeance if he knows the story came from me."

"I promise," said Scrawler.

"Know then," said Kobboltozo, "that the ancestors of the Huggermuggers—the Huggers on the male side, and the Muggers on the female—were men and women not much above the ordinary size—smaller than me, the poor dwarf. Hundreds of years ago they came to this island, directed hither by an old woman, a sort of witch, who told them that if they and their children, and their children's children, ate constantly of a particular kind of shell-fish, which was found in great abundance here, they would continue to increase in size, with each successive generation, until they became proportioned to all other growth in the island—till they became giants—such giants as the Huggermuggers. But that the last survivors of the race would meet with some great misfortune, if this secret should ever be told to more than one person out of the Huggermugger family. I have reasons for believing that Huggermugger and his wife are the last of their race; for all their ancestors and relations are dead, and they have no children, and are likely to have none. *Now there are two persons who have been told the secret. It was told to me, and I tell it to you!*"

As Kobboltozo ended, his face wore an almost fiendish expression of savage triumph, as if he had now settled the giants' fate forever.

"But," said Scrawler, "how came *you* into possession of this tremendous secret; and, if true, why do you wish any harm to happen to the good Huggermuggers?"

"I hate them!" said the dwarf. "They are rich—I am poor. They are big and well-formed—I am little and crooked. Why should not my race grow to be as shapely and as large as they; for *my* ancestors were as good as theirs, and I have heard that they possessed the island before the Huggermuggers came into it? No! I am weary of the Huggermuggers. I have more right to the island than they. But they have grown by enchantment, while my race only grew to a certain size, and then we stopped and grew crooked. But the Huggermuggers, if there should be any more of them, will grow till they are like the trees of the forest.

"Then as to the way I discovered their mystery. I was taking home a pair of shoes for the giantess, and was just about to knock at the door, when I heard the giant and his wife talking. I crept softly up and listened. They have great voices—not difficult to hear *them.* They were talking about a secret door in the wall, and of something precious which was locked up within a little closet. As soon as their voices ceased, I knocked, and was let in. I assumed an appearance as if I had heard nothing, and they did not suspect me. I went and told Hammawhaxo, the carpenter—a friend of mine, and a dwarf like me. I knew he didn't like Huggermugger much. Hammawhaxo was employed at the time to repair the bottom of a door in the giant's house, where the rats had been gnawing. So he went one morning before the giants were up, and tapped all around the wainscoting of the walls with his hammer, till he found a hollow place, and a sliding panel, and inside the wall he discovered an old manuscript in the ancient Hugger language, in which was written the secret I have told you. And now we will see if the old fortune-teller's prophecy is to come true or not."

15

Mrs. Huggermugger grows thin and fades away

Scrawler, though delighted to get hold of such a story to put into his book, could not help feeling a superstitious fear that the prediction might be verified, and some misfortune befall the good Huggermuggers. It could not come from him or any of his friends, he was sure; for Zebedee Nabbum's first idea of entrapping the giant was long since abandoned. If he was ever to be taken away from the island, it could only be by the force of persuasion, and he was sure that Huggermugger would not voluntarily leave his wife.

Scrawler only hinted then to Huggermugger, that he feared Kobboltozo was his enemy. But Huggermugger laughed, and said he knew the dwarf was crabbed and spiteful, but that he did not fear him. Huggermugger was not suspicious by nature, and it never came into his thoughts that Kobboltozo, or any other dwarf could have the least idea of his great secret.

Little Jacket came now frequently to the giant's house, where he became a great favorite. He had observed, for some days, that Mrs. Huggermugger's spirits were not so buoyant as usual. She seldom laughed—she sometimes sat alone and sighed, and even wept. She ate very little of shell-fish—even her favorite frog had lost its relish. She was growing thin—the once large, plump woman. Her husband, who really loved her, though his manner towards her was sometimes rough, was much concerned. He could not enjoy his lonely supper—he scarcely cared for his pipe. To divert his mind, he would sometimes linger on the shore, talking to the little men, as he called them. He would strip off his long boots and his clothes, and wade out into the sea to get a nearer view of the ship. He could get near enough to talk to them on board. "How should you like to go with us," said the little men, one day, "and sail away to see new countries? We could show you a great deal that you haven't seen. If you went to America with us, you would be the greatest man there."

Huggermugger laughed, but not one of his hearty laughs—his mind was ill at ease about his wife. But the idea was a new one, of going away from giant-land to a country of pygmies. Could he ever go? Not certainly without his wife—and she would never leave the island. Why should he wish to go away? "To be sure," he said, "it is rather lonely here—all our kindred dead—nobody to be seen but little ugly dwarfs. And I really like these little sailors, and shall be sorry to part with them. No, here I shall remain, wife and I, and here we shall end our days. We are the last of the giants—let us not desert our native soil."

Mrs. Huggermugger grew worse and worse. It seemed to be a rapid consumption. No cause could be discovered for her sickness. A dwarf doctor was called in, but he shook his head—he feared he could do nothing. Little Jacket came with the ship's doctor, and brought some medicines. She took them, but they had no effect. She could not now rise from her bed. Her husband sat by her side all the time. The good-hearted sailors did all they could for her, which was not much. Even Zebedee Nabbum's feelings were touched. He told her Yankee stories, and tales of wild beasts—of elephants, not bigger than one of her pigs—of lions and bears as small as lapdogs—of birds not larger than one of their flies. All did what they could to lessen her sufferings. "To think," said Zebedee, "aint it curious—who'd a thought that great powerful critter could ever get sick and waste away like this!"

16

The Sorrows of Huggermugger

At last, one morning while the sailors were lounging about on the beach, they saw the great Huggermugger coming along, his head bent low, and the great tears streaming down his face. They all ran up to him. He sat, or rather threw himself down on the ground. "My dear little friends," said he, "it's all over. I never shall see my poor wife again—never again—never again—I am the last of the Huggermuggers. She is gone. And as for me—I care not now whither I go. I can never stay here—not here—it will be too lonely. Let me go and bury my poor wife, and then farewell to giant-land! I will go with you, if you will take me!"

They were all much grieved. They took Huggermugger's great hands, as he sat there, like a great wrecked and stranded ship, swayed to and fro by the waves and surges of his grief, and their tears mingled with his. He took them in his arms, the great Huggermugger, and kissed them. "You are the only friends left me now," he said, "take me with you from this lonely place. She who was so dear to me is gone to the great Unknown, as on a boundless ocean; and this great sea which lies before us is to me like it. Whether I live or die, it is all one—take me with you. I am helpless now as a child!"

17

Huggermugger leaves his Island

Zebedee Nabbum could not help thinking how easily he had obtained possession of his giant. There was now nothing to do but to make room for him in the ship, and lay in a stock of those articles of food which the giant was accustomed to eat, sufficient for a long voyage.

Huggermugger laid his wife in a grave by the sea-shore, and covered it over with the beautiful large shells which she so loved. He then went home, opened the secret door in the wall, took out the ancient manuscript, tied a heavy stone to it, and sunk it in a deep well under the rocks, into which he also threw the key of his house, after having taken every thing he needed for his voyage, and locked the doors.

The ship was now all ready to sail. The sailors had made a

large raft, on which the giant sat and paddled himself to the ship, and climbed on board. The ship was large enough to allow him to stand, when the sea was still, and even walk about a little; but Huggermugger preferred the reclining posture, for he was weary and needed repose.

During the first week or two of the voyage, his spirits seemed to revive. The open sea, without any horizon, the sails spreading calmly above him, the invigorating salt breeze, the little sailors clambering up the shrouds and on the yards, all served to divert his mind from his great grief. The sailors came around him and told him stories, and described the country to which they were bound; and sometimes Mr. Nabbum brought out his elephants, which Huggermugger patted and fondled like dogs. But poor Huggermugger was often sea-sick, and could not sit up. The sailors made him as comfortable as they could. By night they covered him up and kept him warm, and by day they stretched an awning above him to protect him from the sun. He was so accustomed to the open air, that he was never too cold nor too warm. But poor Huggermugger, after a few weeks more, began to show the symptoms of a more serious illness than sea-sickness. A nameless melancholy took possession of him. He refused to eat—he spoke little, and only lay and gazed up at the white sails and the blue sky. By degrees, he began to waste away, very much as his wife did. Little Jacket felt a real sorrow and sympathy, and so did they all. Zebedee Nabbum, however, it must be confessed, "though he felt a kind o' sorry for the poor critter," thought more of the loss it would be to him, as a money speculation, to have him die before they reached America. "It would be too bad," he said, "after all the trouble and expense I've had, and when the critter was so willin', too, to come aboard, to go and have him die. We must feed him well, and try hard to save him; for we can't afford to lose him. Why, he'd be worth at least 50,000 dollars—yes, 100,000 dollars, in the United States." So Zebedee would bring him dishes of his favorite clams, nicely cooked and seasoned, but the giant only sighed and shook his head. "No," he said, "my little friends, I feel that I shall never see your country. Your coming to my island has been in some way fatal for me. My secret must have been told. The prophecy, ages ago, has come true!"

18

The Last of Huggermugger

Mr. Scrawler now thought it was time for him to speak. He had only refrained from communicating to Huggermugger what the dwarf had told him, from the fear of making the poor giant more unhappy and ill than ever. But he saw that he could be silent no longer, for there seemed to be a suspicion in Huggermugger's mind, that it might be these very people, in whose ship he had consented to go, who had found out and revealed his secret.

Mr. Scrawler then related to the giant what the dwarf had told him in the garden, about the concealed MS., and the prophecy it contained.

Huggermugger sunk his head in his hands, and said: "Ah, the dwarf—the dwarf! Fool that I was; I might have known it. His race always hated mine. Ah, wretch! that I had punished thee as thou deservest!

"But, after all, what matters it?" he added, "I am the last of my race. What matters it, if I die a little sooner than I thought? I have little wish to live, for I should have been very lonely in my island. Better is it that I go to other lands—better, perhaps, that I die ere reaching land.

"Friends, I feel that I shall never see your country—and why should I wish it? How could such a huge being as I live among you? For a little while I should be amused with you, and you astonished at me. I might find friends here and there, like you; but your people could never understand my nature, nor I theirs. I should be carried about as a spectacle; I should not belong to myself, but to those who exhibited me. There could be little sympathy between your people and mine. I might, too, be feared, be hated. Your climate, your food, your houses, your laws, your customs—every thing would be unlike what mine has been. I am too old, too weary of life, to begin it again in a new world."

So, MY YOUNG READERS, not to weary you with any more accounts of Huggermugger's sickness, I must end the matter, and tell you plainly that he died long before they reached America, much to Mr. Nabbum's vexation. Little Jacket and his friends grieved very much, but they could not help it, and thought that, on the whole, it was best it should be so. Zebedee Nabbum wished they could, at least, preserve the giant's body, and exhibit it in New York. But it was impossible. All they could take home with them was his huge skeleton; and even this, by some mischance, was said to be incomplete.

Some time after the giant's death, Mr. Scrawler, one day when the ship was becalmed, and the sailors wished to be amused, fell into a poetic frenzy, and produced the following song, which all hands sung, (rather slowly) when Mr. Nabbum was not present, to the tune of Yankee Doodle:—

Yankee Nabbum went to sea
  A huntin' after lions;
He came upon an island where
  There was a pair of giants.
He brought his nets and big harpoon,
  And thought he'd try to catch 'em;
But Nabbum found out very soon
  There was no need to fetch 'em.

Yankee Nabbum went ashore,
  With Jacky and some others;
But Huggermugger treated them
  Just like his little brothers.
He took 'em up and put 'em in
  His thunderin' big fish basket:—
He took 'em home and gave 'em all
  They wanted, ere they asked it.

The giants were as sweet to them
As two great lumps of sugar,—
A very Queen of Candy was
Good Mrs. Huggermugger.
But, ah! the good fat woman died,
The giant too departed,
And came himself on Nabbum's ship,
Quite sad and broken hearted.

He came aboard and sailed with us,
A sadder man and wiser—
But pretty soon, just like his wife,
He sickened and did die, Sir.
But Nabbum kept his mighty bones—
How they will stare to see 'em,
When Nabbum has them all set up
In Barnum's great Museum!

Nothing is clearly known, strange to say, as to what became of this skeleton. In the Museum, at Philadelphia, there are some great bones, which are usually supposed to be those of the Great Mastodon. It is the opinion, however, of others, that they are none other than those of the great Huggermugger—all that remains of the last of the giants.

Note.—I was told, several years since, that Mr. Scrawler's narrative of his adventures in Huggermugger's island, was nearly completed, and that he was only waiting for a publisher. As, however, nothing has as yet been heard of his long expected book, I have taken the liberty to print what I have written, from the story, as I heard it from Little Jacket himself, who is now grown to be a man. I have been told that Little Jacket, who is now called Mr. John Cable, has left the sea, and is now somewhere out in the Western States, settled down as a farmer, and has grown so large and fat, that he fears he must have eaten some of those strange shell-fish, by which the Huggermugger race grew to be so great. Other accounts, however, say that he is as fond of the sea as ever, and has got to be the captain of a great ship; and that he and Mr. Nabbum are still voyaging round the world, in hopes of finding other Huggermuggers.

Kobboltozo: A Sequel to The Last of the Huggermuggers

1

Introduction

Since the publication of The Last of the Huggermuggers, I have received a letter from Mark Scrawler, Esq., who dates from the town of Aristides, Ohio, in which he professes to be very angry that I have published my little story about the giant, particularly as he (who was engaged by Mr. Nabbum to write a full account of every thing) was not even consulted in the case. Mr. Scrawler makes a long letter of it. He complains that his rights have been infringed upon; that he had taken a great deal of trouble in accumulating and arranging his facts, having made copious notes of all that occurred in the giant's island, as well as during the voyage homeward, interspersed with reflections of his own—including some valuable observations on the probable origin of the Huggermugger race, as well as the results of his investigations into shell-fish of the conch and of the bivalve species. "His work," he says, "was progressing slowly, on account of the magnitude of his subject. It would have been one of the most valuable scientific works of the day."

Mr. Scrawler laughs to scorn our slender juvenile publication, which he stigmatizes as "a penny-trumpet affair—a cobweb to catch flies—a flimsy, childish, weak, uncalled-for, not-to-be-thought-of-for-a-moment tissue of absurdities." "Why," he exclaims, "bring out these great scientific facts in the light form of a story-book for children? The sensible Bostonians, New Yorkers, Philadelphians, and all the sensible American citizens in general, demand more solid food. Has, for instance, anything been said in this gilded child's-rattle of a book, of the geology or botany of the giant's island—of the height and breadth of Huggermugger and his wife—of the shape and dimensions of Huggermugger Hall—of Huggermugger's farm-yard—of the vegetables, the fruits, the bread, the meat, the frogs, the fish, and especially of the enormous and singular 'clams' which formed his daily food? Or of the clothes the giants wore, how they were obtained, of what stuff they were woven—and who were Huggermugger's tailors, who his hatters, who his suspender-makers, who taught him English, who supplied him with tobacco, and pipes, and ale? Or has anything been said of the community of dwarfs, of their habits, size, appearance, language, &c., &c.? What presumption," he adds, "for any one to come before the public, (were it only the juvenile public) with such a lame, one-sided, pitiful statement of facts, with nothing to recommend them but the clap-trap trickery and varnish of the story form. The whole thing," he says, "is unworthy a man of sense and thought."

Mr. Scrawler intimates that, of course, *he* would have given a very different title to *his* book, and would have shone resplendent on the title-page with a very choice and appropriate motto from Shakspeare—in the following style:—

> "Why man, he doth bestride the narrow world
> Like a Colossus, and we petty men
> Walk under his huge legs"—

after which some *stars*—and then

> *"Upon what meat doth this our Cæsar feed,*
> *That he is grown so great?"*

"Compare a title-page with such a quotation upon it—flaming (he adds with a preternatural poetical fervor,) flaming 'like a star in the forehead of the morning'—compare it with the plain, methodistical style in which you have decked the vacant brow of your weak bantling!"

Mr. Scrawler goes on in this vein, boastful of himself and vituperative of us, and concludes with vaguely hinting at a lawsuit.

In our little story we briefly stated our reasons, in a note, for proceeding to print our account. Some years had elapsed, and Mr. Scrawler's work had not appeared. We heard also, from pretty good authority, that he had shown portions of his book, as far as it was written, to several publishers, who threw buckets of cold water upon his ardent hopes, and not only declined to publish such "solid"—they even said "heavy"—writing, but advised him outright to discontinue it, and take to something else for a living.

We have also been scolded and threatened in another quarter. Mr. Alonzo Scratchaway, the artist who accompanied the Nabbum expedition, threatens to indict us for stealing his illustrations and spoiling them. He says he intended to have brought out a folio edition (as big as Audubon's Birds) of colored lithograph Hugger-mugger illustrations, designed to accompany Scrawler's work, as an atlas accompanies a geography—"and he'll do it yet, whether Scrawler publishes or not. None of your petty wood-cuts," says Scratchaway, "but something as grand and original as Retsch, or Flaxman, or Gustave Doré."

Here I believe we get to the end of our troubles on the score of our (as we thought) inoffensive little book. We believe that Mr. Zebedee Nabbum has not yet complained of misrepresentation as to his character or dialect; that Little Jacket (or Mr. John Cable) does not look otherwise than favorably on our narrative of his curious adventures, and that Mr. Barnum is above imputing any ill feeling in the allusions we have made to his name.

2

Two Old Comrades go off together

Presuming that our young readers are acquainted with the giants' story alluded to in the foregoing chapter, I will now proceed to give a narrative of what occurred in the island, after the departure thence of Huggermugger and the American sailors—and I will state before I am through, how I came to obtain my information.

The reader will recollect that it was thought by some that Little Jacket (or John Cable, as he has for some time been called) went out West, and settled down as a farmer; while it was reported by others that he was still cruising with Mr. Nabbum in search of the wonderful. There is a basis of truth in both accounts. John Cable went out West, and thinking himself tired of a sea life, turned farmer for a while, during which he grew to be a good deal stouter and taller. But the old love of sea life returned, and he gave up farming, and came to New York to see what advantageous employment might be found on board some good ship. Here it chanced that he fell in once more with his old comrade, Nabbum, who was just about making another voyage of discovery. The long and the short of it is, that Jacky Cable and Zebby Nabbum sailed together, secretly intending to visit once more the giant's island.

There were no particular incidents worth noting on board ship. The voyage was a pretty long one. I believe they touched at the Cape of Good Hope and the Island of Madagascar. At last the island of the giants loomed in the distance.

As they drew near the coast, Zebedee sighed to think what a great speculation failed when Huggermugger died. Jacky, too, sighed, but it was to think how lonely it would be there now, and how changed, since the good giant and giantess were no more. Now, they should see no one but the dwarfs, with the spiteful Kobboltozo perhaps made king of the island.

They determined, however, to travel into the interior of the island, and to ascertain how things had gone on since their departure. Having cast anchor in a secure bay, Nabbum and Jacky went ashore in a boat, and landed near the well-known beach where the great shells were. They took with them provisions for several days' journey, and proceeded by the nearest road towards Huggermugger Hall and the neighboring village of the dwarfs. They encountered the usual difficulties in clambering over the great rocks and pushing their way through the tall shrubs and weeds. They found, too, many things to wonder at, which they did not recollect having noticed before. High over their heads waved great palms and magnolia trees—enormous grasshoppers sprang by them—gigantic butterflies flashed overhead, their wings blazing with purple and gold. Birds as big as eagles darted from tree to tree, singing as loud as hand-organs, and filling the trackless woods with their strange jargon. Nabbum compared it to an immense giant menagerie, and Jacky said it reminded him of some monster concert about to commence, when from the double basses up to the octave flutes, all the musicians in the orchestra were running up and down the scales on their instruments, and all the people in the pit talking at the top of their voices at the same time. Then there were huge flowers that flaunted over their heads, loading the air with thick perfume—some like banners, scarlet, orange, and blue—some that hung their bells, like great church-bells, which even seemed to be vibrating sometimes with a low ringing, weighed down and swinging with the weight of the enormous bees that hummed inside with their bagpipe drone. Now they would pass near a marsh, where the frogs were plunging in their noontide bath, or croaking with voices like young bull-calves. Now their way lay near enormous ravines which one might fancy the favorite haunts of the boa-constrictor and rattlesnake—but there were no poisonous reptiles in the island, for the Huggermugger race (like St. Patrick) had long since exterminated them—and now they would climb a hill, from which they could see afar the top of Huggermugger Hall, looming like an enchanted castle. Ah! there was no Huggermugger to take them there in his basket—no Mrs. Huggermugger to welcome them to her hospitable dwelling.

3

Messrs. Nabbum and Cable find things changed in the Giant's Island

After a rather fatiguing tramp, our two travellers reached the deserted mansion. On approaching, they saw that the front door was wide open. They at once suspected that Kobboltozo, or some of the dwarfs were there, and had taken possession of the house. Perhaps they had made havoc of all that the giant had left behind him. They ascended the stairs, but saw no one. There was little change since they had left. But how dreary seemed the great mansion, without the good host and hostess who had once entertained them there! There was something very desolate in such a great house being forevermore untenanted. There stood the two great arm-chairs at either side of the huge chimney, and on the mantel-piece there was still the great shell in which Jacky was brought to the giant's house. There was the table at which the giant and giantess had sat. There was the bed where Mrs. Huggermugger had died. There were her huge scissors, and knitting-needles, and distaff—there even her dresses hanging on the wall. There were the old boots that had waded through the marshes, and the old fish-basket that had brought home so many muscles,* and oysters, and clams. And high above all was

*A friend suggests that it was probably a species of *muscle* on which our giant friends fed, which naturally might have contributed to the increase of their limbs. Another suggests that in their religious creed they might have been *mussulmen*. But I think my friends were joking.

the great window—like an immense studio-window, pouring down a flood of light upon all. Now the Huggermuggers' tramp-tramp was no more heard through the corridors—the wreaths of curling pipe-smoke no more arose to the rafters—the great voices no more came rumbling from room to room—the uproarious laughter was forever silent.

Our visitors roamed about the house with mingled feelings of curiosity and sadness. They expected every moment to meet some of the dwarfs, but found no traces of any living being. All was silent as the grave. Now and then the chirp of a solitary cricket resounded under the desolate hearthstone, like the shrill noise of some one filing. A melancholy big robin sang in the neglected garden outside, and it seemed like a requiem over the departed; and overhead they heard the long wail of the locust, swelling and dying like a bell through the still summer air. Every thing within and without was desolate, deserted, neglected. But there were signs of some one's having been there since their departure. Not only was the outer door found open, but the floor of the great hall was scattered over here and there with fragments as of a feast,—plates, dishes, bottles, and dry scraps of food were found, which had evidently belonged to the dwarfs, and on the hearth were the remains of half-burnt brands, and cooking utensils of much too diminutive a pattern to have served the giants.

Our two adventurers left the giant's house, and proceeded towards the village of the dwarfs, expecting every moment to meet some one who would give them some information of what had passed. But they saw no one. They reached at length the village, but found all deserted—not the trace of a living creature. The houses were all forlorn and neglected—some of them without doors, or windows, or chimneys—the fences half fallen, the gate-hinges rusty and broken, great burdocks and thorn-apples and other rank weeds of enormous size growing over and almost concealing them, and every thing evincing the most utter desolation. They went up and down, searching in vain for some living being. They called, but no one answered. At last they saw some one appear at the door of one of the huts, peeping timidly out, and a wan little* figure appeared and came out to meet them.

This little figure was the dwarf Stitchkin, the tailor. Our friends remembered him, though they did not at first recognize him. This little tailor had been sometimes employed to make Huggermugger's clothes; but having been obliged to look up to such a height when he measured the giant, he always foreshortened his figure, and consequently made his coats excessively short in the waist; so that Mrs. H. persuaded her husband to employ him no longer, at least to make his coats. The little man seemed glad to see our friends back again. When questioned about the disappearance of the rest of the dwarfs, and the dilapidated state of their village, the tailor sighed and said: "My friends, it is my belief that they are all gone—dead or lost—and that I am the only survivor of the dwarfs."

"And Kobboltozo," said Jacky, "what has become of him?"

"I know not," said Stitchkin, "and yet—it is a long story and

*It must be remembered that we measure by the giant scale. We call the dwarfs little, because they were so in comparison with Huggermugger.

very singular one. If you wish, you shall hear it. But come, let us leave this wretched place, and seat ourselves under yonder great tree; and there, in the cool shade, I will tell you all I know of the history of Kobboltozo and the other of my race."

So the three went and seated themselves on the grass under the trees, and after Mr. Nabbum had treated the tailor to some luncheon, out of the provisions he had brought with him from the ship, and refreshed him with a bottle of good ale, Stitchkin gave the narrative from which we compile the following singular history.

4

How Kobboltozo bore the Giant's departure

You know (said Stitchkin) that we small people are looked upon by you foreigners as a hard-natured, selfish race of beings. I think it must be true, for none of my tribe ever did *me* any kindness that I know of, and I have always found it very difficult to live among them. I was somehow different from them all. I made clothes for them, but half the time they didn't pay me; so that I was poor and oppressed, and lonely, while those around me were flourishing and happy.

But none of them were as bad as Kobboltozo. He never was liked by any of us. I dare say you know that he was the cause of Huggermugger's misfortunes and departure. When the giant went away in your ship, he could not repress his joy.

He had watched with malicious delight the preparations making for Huggermugger's departure. He sat on a rock, from which he saw the giant go aboard the ship. He saw the sailors receive him on deck—he saw them hoist their sails, and lingered till the ship was out of sight. He then snapped his fingers, grinned with satisfaction, stood up, danced, and sang a snatch of barbarous melody.

"Aha!" he said, "Old Hugg, you are safe now. *You'll* never come back—*you* will never arrive at the country of these foolish sailors—you'll die on board, and they'll chuck you overboard, and give your great carcass to the sharks. *Your* fate is settled, I think. Hurrah! The dwarfs, as you called us, will be kings of the island; and who knows but some of us may yet grow to be as great as the Huggermuggers!"

So saying, Kobboltozo almost turned a summerset in his delight. Returning homeward, he met some of his friends, and told them they had seen the last of Huggermugger. They knew that the giant had gone, and were in as great glee as the shoemaker.

"Come," said Kobboltozo, "what shall we do? suppose we have a great feast, and a carouse?"

"Agreed!" cried the dwarfs. "Let's go and summon all our neighbors, and their wives and children, and tell the good news—that the giant has gone, and the island is ours. Then for the feast—where shall it be? where shall it be?"

"Suppose we have it in Huggermugger Hall," said Kobboltozo.

"Agreed!" said they all. And there was a general scrambling and tumbling over the great rocks and stones, and a plunging through the bushes; and while some ran to summon their neighbors, others made their way to the giant's house, and crowded up to the door. To their great disappointment, however, they found it shut and locked. Whereupon ensued a tremendous hubbub. Some swore, others banged with their sticks, others brought stones and tried to batter the door, others proposed to set fire to it. At last Keholo, the locksmith, thought he could pick the lock. So they brought a ladder and placed it against the huge portal, and Keholo mounted with the biggest instruments he could procure for the purpose. The crowd was very impatient, but in the course of an hour the huge fastening, which was of simple construction, (for Huggermugger being perfectly unsuspicious and fearless of the dwarfs, never thought a complicated lock necessary, and in fact seldom locked his door at all, but kept open house to all,) gave way—and the door, with the crowd all pressing at once against it, slowly opened. In rushed the crowd, and up the great stone steps they mounted—they were accustomed to climbing—and entered the great hall. The solemn silence of the place would have been oppressive to any but these hard-natured beings; and indeed there were some among them who felt it—some who had looked up to the giant with awe and respect, even with admiration—some who, if they did not love, at least did not hate him—some who had had good reason to remember him as a protector and benefactor. These felt ill at ease in this great house. What right had they to be there? How could Huggermugger's departure benefit them?—and why should they assemble here—why hold here a feast to celebrate the absence of the rightful lord and proprietor of the domain—of him to whom this house, this whole island was fitted, far better than for them?

However, as is usual in such cases, the majority overruled the minority, and the few who at first felt a reluctance to join the mob, soon found themselves carried along with the multitude in the excitement of the occasion.

5

The Feast of the Dwarfs

Having dragged up stairs the ladder, the dwarfs bore it with them into the great hall, and raised it against the table, which stood in the centre of the room. There was great talking and shouting and laughing as they mounted the table, and capered to and fro upon it.

"Ha, ha!" they cried, "only think of it—the giant's house is ours—the island is ours—the dwarfs are kings of the land—every thing is ours! Hurrah! Quick—let us have our feast here, on this very table—ere sundown!"

So while some ran out to bring bread and meat, and fish and vegetables, and fruits and plates, and knives and forks, and spoons and tumblers, others dragged out one of the giant's saucepans, and lit a fire on the hearth, and began preparations for cooking. All found something to do. The women were as active as the men. Whatever they could fetch ready-cooked from their houses, they brought; and whatever could serve them in the giant's house, they unscrupulously used. What chiefly delighted them was the discovery of some bottles of ale, and also a half empty beer-barrel, which they contrived to tap and set its contents flowing. The bottles they could not so easily manage, as they were very tightly corked.

When the feast was ready, they all mounted upon the table, and seated themselves at the banquet. Kobboltozo, as president, opened the feast with a speech, in which he congratulated his friends on the departure of Huggermugger, and the possession of the giant's house and island by the dwarfs.

"Friends," he said, "let us hail with joy this auspicious day. He who once lorded it over us, the giant whom we feared—he who by reason of his tremendous size could not fail to be a tyrant over us smaller people, has gone—gone forever, let us hope, and the island belongs to us. Now we are all free and equal. No one can say, 'I am greater than my neighbor.' Every one is at liberty to act as he pleases. What doubt is there that we shall now prosper in our affairs, and all grow rich—all grow powerful?

"Friends, I propose a toast: 'Hurra for liberty and equality, and each man for himself.' "

So they all fell to eating and drinking. There was great merriment and noise. Pretty soon the strong giant-beer got into their heads, and the feast became a wild orgy. They shouted, they laughed, they embraced, they stood up, they danced, they turned summersets among the plates and glasses, they quarrelled and pelted each other—nothing could exceed the wild reckless extravagance of this feast.

Presently some one proposed to drink Huggermugger's health, in a bottle of his own ale. There was a general roar of assent. "What a capital idea—ha, ha! drink the giant's health and a long voyage to his highness!—drink his health in his own ale—ha, ha! *He'll* never drink it again. Come, some of you, help me get this big bottle on the table! yo-heave-o!—once more! up with him—there! But how shall we get the cork out? Can anybody find Huggermugger's cork-screw?"

"O, but don't you see," said another, "it's only fastened in with ropes. Here, bring your hatchet, Hammawhaxo!" and the carpenter soon cut the ropes which held the huge cork. But the dwarfs did not know what frisky ale this was—for no sooner were the fastenings cut, than fz—z—zzzffzFFFZZ—POPP!!!! out flew the cork into their faces, knocking over some half dozen of them, who lay insensible for some time, and out foamed the frothy ale, deluging and nearly drowning a half dozen more, wetting nearly every one from head to foot, and streaming in torrents down from the table.

This unlucky adventure rather sobered the company for a while, and they concluded to let the other bottles alone.

One foolish fellow, however, who had drank quite enough, and who had left the festive scene to take a stroll around the room, thought he saw on a small table in a corner a vessel containing water; so whether he instantly became very thirsty, or wished to wash the ale off his face, he climbed upon the table, and approaching the vessel thrust his head into it—but he lost his balance and tumbled half way in. It was Huggermugger's inkstand—and the dwarf had some difficulty in getting out. When he did so, his head and one half his body was ink-black, while the other was its original color. He did not dare to show himself to his friends in this plight, so he slunk into a dark corner till the feast should break up.

Another half-tipsy deserter of the jovial company, happening to see a rat-trap open, and still baited with cheese (the rats themselves seemed to have all disappeared since the giant's departure) walked straight into it—when down went the iron gratings, and he was caught. Becoming alarmed, he called to his companions—but it was some time before anybody came; when they did, they danced around the cage, laughing at him, and poking him with sticks, and it was some time before the poor fellow was let out.

Meanwhile the sun went down, the twilight stole on, and still they kept up the revel. The moon rose and shone in through the great window, and they had no need of candles. As the night advanced, however, the sky became overcast. Distant thunder was heard. Wild masses of dark cloud drifted across the moon, which now shone bright, now was buried in the clouds. The revelry was at its wildest, when a nearer peal of thunder startled and sobered some of the more timorous. Something nearer and darker than a cloud seemed to overshadow them—and looking up at the great window, what should they see, or fancy they saw, but the great faces of the Huggermuggers between them and the moon, gazing sorrowfully down upon them. The panic spread at once. Rushing, scrambling, tumbling over each other, pitching almost head-foremost down from the table, away they scampered as fast as they could in their tipsy condition. Fast as they could they made for the door, and fled in the desperation of fear, rolling and tumbling down the stairs—and not one was left behind, save Kobboltozo and his friend Hammawhaxo, the carpenter. They alone were sober, cool, and collected. Besides, they had a motive for remaining, and were not sorry that they were left alone in the hall of the Huggermuggers.

6

The Search of Kobboltozo and Hammawhaxo

The great room was no sooner cleared of the frightened dwarfs, than Kobboltozo and Hammawhaxo each lit a candle, and approached the secret closet in which the ancient Hugger manuscript had been discovered. What their object was I will tell you.

When Hammawhaxo first saw this old manuscript, (the Huggermuggers were living in their house then, you may remember,) he had no time to peruse it thoroughly, but only got a hasty look into it, for he was afraid of being detected by the giant and his wife. But he read enough to learn the fatal secret, the divulging of which is supposed to have been the cause of the misfortunes which befell them. He read, you remember, that the Huggermugger race had become great by eating of a particular kind of shell-fish, while the dwarfs stopped growing at a certain period, and began to grow crooked. Also, that if this secret were told to more than one person out of the Huggermugger family, some great calamity would befall the last survivor of the race. This secret the carpenter, (who perhaps did not bear any positive malice towards the giant,) in a heedless hour, imparted to the shoemaker.

But it was not enough for Kobboltozo that he had ruined the giant's happiness. He imagined that it was a possible thing to become a giant himself. He could not bear to live and die a dwarf. He would have given all that he owned, and all the little heart and soul that he had, to boot, to be able to stand in Huggermugger's shoes, to put on Huggermugger's boots and stride as he did across the country. To be Huggermugger's equal—to be able to thunder in a voice like his, and sit in his great arm-chair—to make the other dwarfs bow down like slaves before him—to rule in the island by fear, and not as the good giant did, by justice and kindness, was his constant ambition and dream. Now, since the giant was gone, it became his darling *hope*.

"That manuscript," he said to himself, "at which the carpenter got but a glimpse, must contain more secrets worth knowing. Where is this mysterious shell-fish—what is it? Why should not I profit by it? And how long would it take to grow out of my dwarfish limits into strong exulting gianthood?" Such thoughts burned in the cobbler's heart day and night, and gave him no rest. He did not see that true greatness is far from consisting in size or the possession of power.

"And now, at last," he thought, "my way is clear. I shall obtain the old manuscript and shall know all. If my fate condemns me to be no bigger, no handsomer than I am, I must submit; but if this manuscript holds out any hope, be sure I shall not be slow in availing myself of it."

So Kobboltozo was not sorry that his companions had been

frightened away, for the night and solitude were favorable to his schemes. He would have preferred, perhaps, to be entirely alone, and that none should know the full contents of the manuscript but himself. But he could do nothing without Hammawhaxo; first in finding the sliding panel in the wall, and secondly in helping him to decipher the ancient Hugger writing. So it was previously agreed that the carpenter should remain.

With eager steps they hastened to the door of the secret closet, and with trembling hands pushed back the sliding panel. But to their great surprise and vexation they found nothing there. For it will be remembered that the giant had taken it out before his departure, and sunk it in a deep well under the rocks. At first Kobboltozo was disposed to think that his friend had deceived him with a false story, but this idea soon passed, and on reflection he concluded that the giant had concealed it somewhere else. He was almost certain that Huggermugger had not taken it with him, for he had seen him carry scarcely any thing to the ship.

Swallowing down his disappointment then as well as he could, he proposed to Hammawhaxo that they should commence searching the whole house. Hammawhaxo, though not so solicitous about the matter as his friend, consented to help him. So they went first round and round the room, tapping on the walls, poking into all the closets, and cracks, and corners. Then they went into all the other rooms, peeping into drawers, and boxes, and chests—turning things upside down and inside out—ransacking from garret to cellar. Sometimes they would light on some old scrap of parchment, yellow with age, and from which the writing was almost faded. But they could make out nothing. As near as could be guessed, they were only fragments of old love-letters that had passed between the giant and his wife—how many years ago, who knows?

In fine, the dwarfs looked everywhere except down the well, where the Hugger manuscript was soaking; and which, if they could ever have succeeded in fishing up, would have been so faded and blurred, that they could never have read a line of it.

Meanwhile, the thunder, which had rolled heavily in the distance, came nearer and nearer. Through the great windows the lightning blazed, almost extinguishing the light of their feeble candles. The carpenter became uneasy, and proposed that they should abandon their search for that night, as it was evident a storm was fast coming on.

"We had better go," said he, "we can come again to-morrow. It is more comfortable at home than in this dreary great castle. The rain will be pouring down soon. Hark! how the wind roars in the trees and on the roof. Come!"

"Presently," said Kobboltozo. "There is one place we have not yet thoroughly explored. I thought I noticed a little door at one end of the cellar. It may be that the manuscript is hid there. Let us take one look; we shan't be but a moment. It would be a pity not to look. To-morrow we may not have so good a chance; for the dwarfs will be again here, lounging about, and we must conceal our purposes from them."

So, much to the carpenter's reluctance, they descended the steps to the cellar, each with a blazing torch in his hand. They went along till they came to a corner, where Kobboltozo fancied he had seen the little door. And, sure enough, there was a door, just large enough for them to creep through. They easily drew back the bolt, and after a few stout tugs, the door, which from the cobwebs about it appeared to have been long closed, opened, and they peeped in. It seemed to be a low vaulted cell of some length. They entered, and crept cautiously along. The floor soon began to slope downwards; but they still groped along till they came to steps. Descending these, they were stopped by another door, much larger than the first. They deliberated some time whether they should open it. Hammawhaxo was for returning; Kobboltozo for going on.

"Just this door," he said; "we will just peep in, and if we don't find what we want, we will return." So he slid back the bolt of this door also, and with a push it yielded. They entered, and found themselves in a very large cave, hewn out of the solid rock. There seemed to be nothing in it—but on the walls, as well as they could see by the light of their flickering torches, were inscriptions in huge letters, of the ancient Hugger language, cut in the walls. These excited their curiosity. "Perhaps," said Kobboltozo, "these inscriptions will tell us something about the mysterious shell-fish." So they went round and round, trying to decipher them. But the letters were so large, and reached up so high in the darkness, and their torches threw so dim a light, that they could not make out a single word.

"Come," said Kobboltozo, at last, "let's go now; we shall discover nothing to-night. We can return to this place to-morrow and continue our search. Why, really, the storm is coming. I can hear the wind and the thunder even through these thick walls."

They turned to retrace their steps, but a sudden gust of wind from some door or crevice blew violently against them, and in an instant both their torches were extinguished.

7

Gropings under Ground

The two dwarfs groped round and round the great cave, but could not find the door by which they entered. "What the deuce shall we do?" they said; "this is a most unfortunate business!" "Why didn't you look well where the door was?" said one. "Why didn't you return before the wind arose!" said the other. "Why did you stop to look at those letters on the wall?" said the carpenter; "you knew you couldn't read them!" "Why didn't you bring along some matches to relight our torches?" said the cobbler. "And why didn't you bring a covered lantern?" said the carpenter. "If you had only had your wits about you," said the cobbler, "you would have taken a better look into that manuscript, and ascertained where the wonderful shell-fish were to be found, and then we needn't have got ourselves into this hole!"

"Confound your old manuscript, with the shell-fish," said the carpenter. "I wish to heavens I had never seen it, or told you any thing about it, and then I should have been safe and snug in my bed at home!"

And so grumbling at each other, they groped about in the impenetrable darkness; and instead of helping and sympathizing with each other, selfish beings that they were, they did nothing but lay the cause of their misfortune on each other's shoulders.

At last they found in the darkness an opening, which they supposed was the door. But they were mistaken. It was only another passage, leading them still further underneath the ground. There was nothing to do now but wait till morning, or go on groping their way in the darkness, hoping by and by to reach an opening in the rocks by which they might extricate themselves from this gloomy and dangerous place. Gloomy it certainly was, and, for aught they knew, dangerous, for they were fearful every moment of plunging headlong into some deep hole or well.

After awhile, finding no outlet, and fearing to go on, they concluded to sit or lie down, and wait patiently for the morning light—if indeed the morning light ever came into that dark labyrinth. So they sat down and waited, with their backs against the damp sides of the cavern. The night seemed endlessly long. At last they thought they perceived a faint, dim light, so they continued their way. Sometimes the passage grew wide and high; sometimes it was so low and narrow that they could hardly squeeze through. At length it grew gradually wider and higher, and descended rapidly. Soon it began to grow less dark, and they could see the roofs of the winding galleries through which they passed hung with stalactites and crystals. It continued to grow lighter, but with a tinge as of a distant firelight, not the clear white sunshine. What could this be? was it a subterranean fire they were approaching?

Larger and more splendid became the hanging stalactites and

crystals. Great blocks of marble—white, green, and red—of porphyry, jasper, malachite, agate, carnelian, lapis lazuli, lay heaped in confusion around. And now the walls and ceilings were all powdered and frosted over with marble and silver—now glowed with crystallizations of copper, platina, or zinc;—and now it was all gold—gold growing and branching out into every sort of fantastic design—gold blossoming like fern or coral, or clinging to the stone like sponges or fungi—gold streaking and veining the rocks. And now, behold, all manner of precious stones, that seemed to blossom like flowers amid the gold and silver leaf-work—flowers of diamond, ruby, carbuncle, emerald, topaz, garnet, sapphire—all glowing more intensely, as the two dwarfs advanced, in the mysterious fire-light which they were approaching.

There seemed to be no end to these gorgeous chambers and galleries. Sometimes, tempted by the splendor of these gold plants and gems, they endeavored to tear or break off a branch of the metal leaves, or a bunch of diamonds or rubies. It resisted all their efforts, and they were forced to leave it. They were lost in wonder at all this strange and unheard of magnificence. "Have we then reached the centre of the earth," they thought, "and are these the secret laboratories and treasure-houses of the earth?"

At last they approached a great door, gorgeous to behold, before which hung what appeared to be a great curtain of pure gold-leaf and amber, inwrought with thousands of diamonds, and sapphires, and rubies. This curtain seemed to be semi-transparent, and it was behind this and through this that the great red light was glowing, which they had seen so far off among the caves.

The dwarfs raised one corner of this curtain and entered. They were struck dumb with wonder and amazement at what they saw.

8

The Gnomes

It was the dwelling and laboratory of those elfs who work under ground—called Gnomes.

The dwarfs found themselves in a vast hall or dome, in the centre of which seemed to be a huge furnace, from which issued great flames. But what was very strange, they could feel no heat, they could hear no crackling, they could see no smoke. The flames were like those of the Northern-lights, only redder and intenser—indeed, so intense that the dwarfs who had been so long in the darkness, could hardly bear to look at them. On drawing nearer, they were astonished to see against the light, swarms of little beings of strange and grotesque shapes, and all of one sober brown or grey color, like the rocks around, and all busily and silently at work. Some were melting or refining metals, and shutting and opening the doors of the furnace—some dragging out great lumps of what seemed to be red-hot iron—some ladling out melted gold and silver—some hammering at anvils—some filing and polishing precious stones of enormous size and wonderful lustre—some digging into the solid rock-crystal sides of the great hall—some heaving and rolling along great fragments of stone—some descending and ascending mines and holes in the earth—all busy, and active, and quick; not one idle; each one seeming to know his task, and, though it might puzzle you to imagine what it was all for, each one working in perfect silence.

As Kobboltozo and Hammawhaxo approached, no one stopped working—they merely raised a moment their queer little eyes to look at them, but didn't turn their heads. They showed no signs of curiosity or astonishment, but seemed to look at them with as much indifference as if they were quite accustomed to them. One could not compare them to any thing so truly, as to a swarm of magnified brown ants. There was the same running to and fro, each on his own special business, yet for the good of the community, the same indifference to any thing else than the work before them—the same silence—the same swarming multitudinous life. They would appear and disappear, one couldn't tell how. They would come up from some hole or crack in the earth—they would run up the sides of the room—they would drop down from the ceiling, and go on working as before. They would lift objects of enormous size and weight. Nothing seemed impossible to them. One after another they swarmed up from the crevices in the rocks, carrying on their backs huge pieces of ore or crystal, which they ran to deposit in a corner where there was an immense pile of treasures—and then would descend to appear again with fresh burdens.

All this caused immense astonishment to our friends the shoemaker and carpenter. They had never seen such curious little beings as these. They had never seen any work done so silently, so cleverly.

After they had looked on with wondering eyes for some time, they began to think that they would enter into conversation with the gnomes, and perhaps learn from them, who seemed to have explored all the secrets under ground, how they should get out of the earth. Indeed Kobboltozo thought he might kill two birds with one stone, and make some inquiries with regard to the wonderful shell-fish.

They therefore came up to a goodnatured-looking little imp, who was engaged in crystallizing a lump of silver, and asked him as politely as they could, if he could tell them the way back to the surface of the earth. The gnome only looked at him with his twinkling jet eyes, and without speaking, or even pointing with his ever-busy hands, simply nodded in a certain direction. They then asked him if he knew where they could find a certain shell-fish, which would make men grow to be giants. The gnome stared, and faintly smiled, and nodded in the same direction. This was all they could get from him. They tried others of the gnomes, who all repeated the same nod of the head, in the same direction.

"From all which," said Kobboltozo, "it seems we must take that way indicated by these queer silent creatures, if we wish to get out of this place. I think we had better be off, as soon as we can. The truth is, I am getting to be confoundedly hungry, notwithstanding last night's feast. Suppose we ask one of our little fairy friends for a bit of bread and cheese. Hallo there! you young lump of brown earth, with the big head and arms—couldn't you give a starving fellow-creature of the upper-crust, a bit of something—we won't be particular—any thing just to keep body and soul together, for we are almost famished. But I fancy you don't raise potatoes and pumpkins down here—eh, young one?"

The gnome only stared at him and passed on.

"You, then!" cried Kobboltozo, "you with the smutty face and the hairy legs—can't you give us something to eat—don't you ever eat down here?" And the shoemaker and the carpenter both made signs to show that they had great appetites.

But the gnome stared as the other did, and passed on.

"By jingo!" said the carpenter, "I believe they are deaf and dumb, or don't know what meat and drink means, any more than rest or sleep. Come, let's be off; we shall get no satisfaction out of these creatures."

So they proceeded in the way so vaguely indicated by the gnomes, and soon found themselves in a gallery which led them through several such caverns as those they had already traversed. Gradually the red fire-light which issued from the hall of the gnomes grew fainter and fainter, till they found themselves at last in utter darkness. Soon, however, a faint light, as from without, seemed to dawn, dimly revealing the rough sides of the cavern. Encouraged, they pushed on through the narrow windings—now up, now down—now interrupted in their journey by huge masses of fallen rock, now by streams of water—till to their great joy they at last reached an opening in the side of a rocky gorge, from which they saw the sunlight again, and the blue sea sleeping beneath them.

STAMPEDE OF THE DWARFS.

KOBBOLTOZO ASKS FOR SOMETHING TO EAT.

THE WITCH'S CAVE.

THE SCRABBLE FOR SHELL-FISH.

9

The Witch's Cave

This opening, in which they emerged, proved to be a small cave, which had the appearance of having once been inhabited. The walls and ceiling were a good deal smoked. There was an opening which had evidently served as a chimney, and a piece of an old rusty lamp which had been fastened to the wall still remained. But whoever had lived there, it must have been centuries since, they thought, for not only weeds, and grass, and flowers, but moss and lichens were growing abundantly on the rocks and between the stones. In one corner they thought they saw something resembling remains of human bones, half buried beneath the earth. But what interested Kobboltozo was to discover on one side of the cave a rude, half-effaced inscription, in letters not unlike those in the great cavern where they had lost their way. What could this place be? What was the mysterious connection between this cave, and the region of the gnomes, and the dwelling of the giants? Suddenly a thought flashed across Kobboltozo's brain, and he ran to the opening of the cave, and looked out to discover on what part of the island they were. The cave opened upon a narrow and steep ravine, down which there were rude steps, not easy to ascend or descend, leading from the cave's mouth to the bottom of the rocks, whence a path conducted to the sea-shore.

Kobboltozo having made this discovery, came running back to his companion in a state of great excitement.

"It is—it is the very place!" he cried. "A lucky star has guided us to this spot! Know then, my friend, that this is the Witch's Cave—that very witch who came with the ancestors of the Huggermuggers to this island, and who foretold to them the growth and prosperity of their race."

For you must know that there was a tradition among the dwarfs that such a witch had formerly lived somewhere in this very gorge. But no one had ever ventured up the difficult steps, or had discovered the place of her abode. A sort of superstitious fear, too, had effectually deterred them from entering this wild and gloomy ravine.

"We have found it—we have found it!" cried Kobboltozo; "there's no doubt of this being the place. Ever since you told me of your glimpse at the secret of the giant race, I have thought of this ancient witch, and the tradition of this ravine. And to think that our bad luck in getting lost leads us to this spot, and turns out to be good luck after all. Aha! I begin to see! Was it then by this long dark labyrinth through which we have passed, that the witch held communication with those gnomes—those queer goblins of the earth? And was it these gnomes who helped the Huggermuggers to build their house?"—

"And these letters on the wall—what are they? Come, Hamm, you are a bit of a scholar. Help me to spell out what remains of the inscription."

"Willingly," said the other, "but I fear, Kobb, that we can't get much satisfactory information from these half-effaced characters."

"We'll try, at any rate," said the shoemaker.

So they set their wits together, but found themselves much puzzled to spell out any thing clearly. All they could make of it was something like this translation:—

. . . . CAVE OF THE SEA . . . .
UND . . ROCKS . . . . . . RIGHT HAND . . .
. . . . . . SHELL FI . . . . . . MER-KING . .
. . . WAVES . . . STILL . . . . . . GIANT . .

"Well, but this is something, at any rate," said Kobboltozo. "It gives some clue to what we are seeking. It seems we must find a Cave of the Sea, lying somewhere under the rocks, to the right hand, after we have descended the ravine; that there we may find the shell-fish. But what is this about the mer-king, and the waves? Must we call up the mer-king, and ask him where the wonderful shell-fish are? Yes, that must be it—and it must be done when the waves are perfectly still. We'll do it."

"But," said the carpenter, "we must have an incantation."

"What's that?" said the shoemaker.

"Why, some sort of spell, or rhyme, and something scattered on the waves, while we repeat a verse or so, or some old words of the Hugger language. I hardly know—but I've heard that that's the way the witches do. Let's try it. You compliment me on being a bit of a scholar—do you know I'm a bit of a poet too, and often sing my rhymes to myself while I am hammering or planing?"

"Very well; now set your wits agoing, and make some verses for the occasion—a sort of what do you call it—incantation?"

So, half in fun, half in earnest, Hammawhaxo hammered out some lines—and repeated them over to himself till he had got them by heart.

After satisfying themselves that there was nothing else in the witch's cave that could afford them any help in their search, they began the difficult descent of the steep rocks. It was not an easy matter to get down, and several times they came near breaking their necks. But at last they reached the bottom of the gorge. A path, or rather the dry bed of a stream led them down to the sea-shore, where, having allayed their hunger somewhat with some berries they found, they stretched themselves out on the grass under the rocks. There, what with their fatigue and excitement, the cool, soft turf on which they lay, and the soothing murmur of the sea lapping on the beach, they both fell into a profound sleep.

10

Kobboltozo's Dream

Kobboltozo fell asleep with his brain full of witches, mermen, shell-fish, giants, and gnomes. So it was very natural he should dream. And he did dream a wonderful dream, as he afterwards told the carpenter, and which the carpenter (said the tailor) told me. Kobboltozo dreamed that he was walking in the palace of the king of the gnomes. His majesty was bigger than the other gnomes, his subjects, and not at all silent like them; on the contrary, he was very talkative and merry. Kobboltozo asked him, of course, the question which was always uppermost in his mind—where he should find the wonderful shell-fish of the giants.

"That's a secret," said the king, "which no one here knows but myself. It is well you asked me. Come with me."

So they passed through room after room, more splendid than any thing he had yet seen—all was gold, silver, and precious stones—and knocked at a door, which opened, and disclosed a long avenue leading to the sea.

"Take this path," said the king, "and it will conduct you to what you desire—but first fill your pockets with as much gold and as many precious stones as you want." Kobboltozo did so, and bidding the king adieu, the door closed behind him.

Immediately he seemed to have wings to his feet, for he flew in an instant to the sea. When he reached the shore, he found it covered with a strange kind of shell-fish he had never seen. He took one of these, and it opened its shell of itself, as if asking to be eaten. It had a singular but not an unpleasant flavor. So he ate another and another. Presently he began to grow, and grow, and grow. He seemed to be inflating like a balloon, till he found himself larger than Huggermugger, and a good deal handsomer. With huge strides he walked across the island, his pockets full of the gold and jewels the gnome had given him. He reached the village of the dwarfs—and saw his own little workshop, and all the other houses, and all the dwarfs running about pursuing their business, and felt the most supreme contempt for them all, and the most unbounded admiration of himself. It delighted him to see how they ran away from him, or fell on their knees before him, or did whatever he bid them do. "Poor little beings," he said, "I shan't make shoes for you any longer—a greater than Huggermugger is among you—you shall all be my slaves—I will do with you whatever I please—am I not the greatest of the giants?"

(I don't mean to say, said the tailor, that Kobboltozo told all this to Hammawhaxo—it is only what we dwarfs thought he said in his dream.)

Having thrown a few gold pieces to the dwarfs, he strode to the giant's house, and was immensely delighted to find how the great mansion fitted him. Only he would have had it bigger still.

No sooner had he expressed this wish, than the king of the gnomes again stood before him.

"Ah," thought Kobboltozo, "he has come up through those subterranean passages I discovered. He also shall do my bidding." So he told the king to bring him a thousand gnomes, and pull down Huggermugger's house, and build one twice as large. The gnome king nodded, and disappeared. Presently he appeared again, followed by an immense swarm of little brown elfs, who set to work and pulled down the house. Pretty soon they built one twice as large. "Now," said Kobboltozo, "cover it all over with gold and diamonds and rubies." And they brought up gold and diamonds and rubies, and covered the house all over with them. But as they were finishing, they heard thunder, and the witch of the ravine appeared in the midst of the gnomes, with a countenance full of anger, and stamped her foot—when suddenly the gnomes all disappeared and left him alone with the witch.

Kobboltozo rose up to annihilate the old woman with one blow of his mighty arm, when it was suddenly seized by something sharp, which held him fast. Turning around, he found his arm actually caught in the thorns of a great blackberry bush, which in his sleep he had rolled against—and there was an end to his magnificent dream.

11

The Mer-king

Kobboltozo sat up and rubbed his eyes, and looked with intense hatred and disgust at the innocent blackberry bush, which had scratched to pieces his splendid dream. Seeing Hammawhaxo still asleep, he expended upon him a part of his ill-nature in waking him without ceremony. "Come, comrade," he cried, shaking him, "it is time we were going. We have a great deal to do. We must call up the mer-king while the waves are still, and yonder are the rocks where I have no doubt we shall see his cave. Come, get your—what do you call it—incantation all ready. Get up, man—don't be going to sleep again!"

So poor Hammawhaxo was roused up, and followed his companion slowly along the beach towards the rocks. There they were not long in discovering a cave, having a narrow opening on one side to the sea, and an equally narrow entrance from the land. They entered. It was very large and dark, the only light being that which came through the above mentioned opening to the sea. Nearly the whole of the grotto was filled with the water, which appeared to be of immense depth, and of an exquisite emerald green hue. The sea was so quiet that the wavelets hardly whispered against the sides of the dark cavern. It was a weird and solemn place. There was a narrow ledge on which they could walk, and here the two dwarfs took their stand.

"Are you ready with your speech?" said Kobboltozo. "All ready," said his companion. They then threw into the water some shells and bunches of sea-weed, and repeated these lines:—

King of the mysterious sea,
Tell us where the power may be,
Which may set our bodies free
From the enchanter's tyranny.
Where the wondrous food may be
Which will make us great as he
Who was giant here, while we
Are but dwarfs of low degree!

They looked into the deep, clear, emerald water, and waited in silence. At last there was a heaving and a bubbling up from below, and soon a vast, dim, colorless shape, half appearing, half hidden in the green water, waved to and fro beneath them. Then there rose a gigantic head, crowned with magnificent pearls, and coral, and amber, and sea-flowers—an apparition with flowing locks and beard that seemed to mingle with the white foam—and great calm blue eyes that gazed solemnly upon them—and a low voice, in a surfy cadence, chanted this reply:—

Not in the Ocean deep and clear,
Not on the Land so broad and fair,
Not in the regions of boundless Air,
Not in the Fire's burning sphere—
'Tis not here—'tis not there.
Ye may seek it everywhere.
He that is a dwarf in spirit
Never shall the isle inherit.
Hearts that grow 'mid daily cares
Grow to greatness unawares;
Noble souls alone may know
How the giants live and grow.

The water heaved once more in long swells—breaking and sparkling and eddying in the unearthly light of the grotto—as the dim shape disappeared and sunk in the sea.

There was something in the solemnity of the place, and the strange vision, which seemed to impress the words of this reply deeply upon the memory of these two men. But it was more the words than the sense, for it had a meaning they did not altogether comprehend. They turned and left the cave. For some time neither of them spoke a word. They were both sunk in their own thoughts. The appearance of the mer-king had somewhat astonished and awed them; for it was half in jest and unbelief that they had summoned him. The answer disappointed and puzzled them.

"If the wonderful shell-fish," said Kobboltozo, "is not to be found in the sea, nor on the earth, nor in the air, nor in the fire—where the deuce *is* it to be found?"

"Why don't you see?" said Hammawhaxo, "if it isn't to be found *in* the sea, it may be found *on* the sea; if it isn't to be found *on* the ground, it must be *in* or *under* the ground."

"Good! capital!" cried the shoemaker. "Why, Hamm, you have a shrewd wit. I should never have thought of that now. That must be it, without doubt. I'll tell you what, now. We'll divide our labors, and when we've found our treasure we'll divide the profits. You shall pursue your search *on* the sea, and I mine *under* the ground. It's a bargain, isn't it?"

"Well," said the carpenter, "we can try. I must confess I should like the fun of sailing about a little. I always had a sort of hankering after a sea life, and sometimes almost wish I had gone off with those American sailors who were here—though I should have felt rather uneasy, with Huggermugger for a fellow passenger. And as for *you*, old Kobb, you certainly have a fancy for making discoveries under ground. So we'll think about your plan. Let's go home now; we are many miles away from the village, and we must get back before nightfall."

12

The Effects of telling Secrets

Now Hammawhaxo had a wife, and it is very natural for wives to desire to know what has happened, when their husbands are out all night and a great part of next day. Some wives *will* know their husbands' secrets, and *may* not keep them safely locked after they have them.

Mrs. Hammawhaxo (to tell the truth) loved to visit and gossip.

In fine, the best intentioned wives, if they are endowed with a social disposition, will sometimes let a secret escape—not all at once, but little by little, like a leaky bucket.

And so it happened—that which was whispered in the ear was soon buzzed about, and then trumpeted from one house to another, till the whole community of dwarfs knew something of the giant's secret, and of the events we have been narrating.

It was whispered that Kobboltozo and Hammawhaxo had entered into partnership in the oyster and other shell-fish business. And now the whole village was in a state of excitement, and every one was preparing to commence the shell-fish business on his own account. "Is it possible," they said, "that we have been all our lives living here, within reach of this wonderful shell-fish, and have never found it? What wouldn't we give to grow to be giants! We would give all that we have—houses, gardens, trades, wives, children, peace, and happiness—all—to find this wondrous food."

My friends (said Stitchkin) I needn't tell you all the details of this unfortunate business. Look there, at those houses and fences tumbling to pieces—those gardens overgrown with weeds—this whole village deserted and dead. They will tell you more forcibly than I can, the sad fate that befell us.

And yet hardly any of them bore *me* any good will. They laughed at me, or were cold towards me, because I didn't join them or sympathize with them in their mad and ruinous enterprises. And when I did all I could to dissuade them from giving themselves up to a vain and fruitless search, after what I knew they never could find, they treated me as an enemy, and I had no peace or enjoyment as long as they were near me.

As soon as the fatal secret was known, our people began to desert their homes and daily occupations and encamped in numbers near the sea-shore, where they spent days and nights in looking for new species of shell-fish. But they rarely found any. When they did, there was no end to their selfish and envious quarrels. They would wade into the sea, and dig in the sand, and suffer wet and fatigue and hunger all day; and if two or three happened to light at the same time upon any strange bivalve, they would stand and dispute about it all day. Sometimes they organized little companies, and when they had collected a number of shells, some one would steal them and hide them. These companies never held together long. Then each man would seek for himself, and so increase the labor by not having it shared.

Sometimes one fellow would find an enormous clam or oyster, and stand sentinel over it all day, or begin devouring it; or he would deliberately sit down upon it, defending his property, tooth and nail, against all unlawful claimants, and, when night came, carry it off to some secret place.

Did you ever notice a parcel of chickens, when one has found a worm or a bit of mouldy bread? No. 1, the finder, picks up worm and runs, followed hard by No. 2. No. 3 and 4 join in the pursuit, and twenty more. No. 1 drops his worm, which is seized by No. 25. No. 25 is dodged and run down, and relinquishes worm to No. 40, who in turn is persecuted by 45, 46, and 47. Finally, No. 50, being the longest legged and greediest, succeeds in getting ahead of the runners, and bolts down the worm. And so the farce ends, to commence over again the next time a worm turns up.

Just such a farce went on every day among the dwarfs, except that sometimes it turned into a tragedy. Bloody battles sometimes took place among them. Sometimes the waves would wash them away and drown them. Some fell sick, or died from exposure to the hot sun or the damp night air, or from having gormandized upon the shell-fish. Some of them took a fancy, as Kobboltozo did, that the giants' food was to be found in caves, or by burrowing in the earth. Many of them went under ground, and never returned. In fine, all was disorder, strife, and disunion. And, in the mean time, their houses, and shops, and gardens were totally neglected—until all became as you see.

As for myself (said Stitchkin) I remained at home as long as I could; but no one brought me any work, and I became poor. But for all that, I couldn't bear to see my fellow-beings suffer, even through their own folly; and I spent many a night nursing the sick, many a day trying to settle some foolish quarrel, or endeavoring to persuade my neighbors to return to their occupations. I tried to show them that we small people were evidently intended by Providence to be as we are—that mere size did not constitute happiness—that we could not change our natures—that as long as we followed the path allotted to us, we should be happy and prosperous, but while we spent our lives in seeking for the impossible, we should be miserable. Some listened to my advice—when it was too late. Sickness and death had already seized upon them.

"But what became of Hammawhaxo and Kobboltozo?" said Mr. Nabbum.

Neither of them became giants, I believe, (said the tailor). Hammawhaxo had a boat, which he made for himself. He rigged it up with a mast and sail, and, one moonlight night, he and his wife, and a few friends sailed off on a voyage of discovery. His little vessel was seen for some days cruising about, as if seeking for something, then sailed to the north. One day there came on a storm, and he never returned.

As for Kobboltozo, it is not clearly known yet what became of him either. He was seen last entering a cave, which is supposed to lead to vast subterranean chambers. It is said that some others followed him, and found him seated beside a pile of enormous oysters, which he was busily devouring, and that he seemed to be in an unnatural state of jovial excitement, and expressed no intention of returning. Those who saw him left him there, and returned; so that the probability is that he is still under ground, or that he has lost his way and perished.

I have now (said Stitchkin) told you all I know about the fate of our race. In the main, we have brought about our own destruction. But there were some of us who perhaps deserved a better fate—some who regretted the misfortunes of the giants, and looked upon them more as benefactors than as enemies—who, had it not been for the malice and the selfish ambition of Kobboltozo, would still have made good and useful members of our little community.

As for Hammawhaxo, I always thought he had a great deal that was good in him. It was an unfortunate curiosity which made him the first to become acquainted with the giants' secret; and a pardonable want of thought—say even a confiding and unsuspicious nature—which induced him to whisper it in the shoemaker's ear. I can't think he entertained any positive ill will towards Huggermugger. But he erred sadly in having any thing to do with Kobboltozo, after he saw the unhappy results of having imparted to him the secret. He erred in not taking a decided and bold stand against him, rather than siding with him and entering tamely into his schemes.

13

A Surprise

Jacky Cable and Mr. Nabbum thought the tailor's narrative very strange and wonderful; and the latter proposed that they should remain in the island till they had ascertained all the facts about the disappearance and destruction of the dwarfs. "The fact is, Jacky," said Zebedee, "they *wer'nt* dwarfs, except along side of them giants, but were every bit as big as we, and maybe a leetle bigger—and I guess in Ameriky they'd almost take the shine off the Kentucky giant. So you see, I feel a kind o' feller feeling for them, and I for one should like to undertake an exploring expedition in search of some of 'em."

As for Stitchkin, they proposed that he should leave his lonely little house, and come with them on board ship, which the little tailor gladly assented to. So the three left the ruined village and returned to the ship together. The sailors heard the whole story of the dwarfs, and Stitchkin became soon a great favorite among them. Every day some of them would make excursions on shore, under his guidance, where they found enough to do in seeing the wonders of the island.

One day Nabbum, Jacky, and Stitchkin were on shore collecting some of the great shells and other interesting products of the island, when they saw a queer little sailing vessel coming round a projecting point of the rocks, and holding directly towards them. They were much excited, of course, by this apparition, for they supposed they were alone in the island, and couldn't imagine where the little vessel could come from.

"Well now," said Nabbum, "if this aint curous! I want to know! That's about the rummest little craft that ever *I* see. Who do you 'spose is aboard of her?"

"I can't imagine," said Jacky. "I'm prepared now for any thing, after the astonishing stories we've heard. It would take a good deal to surprise me now. If you told me there was a crew of gnomes aboard, with an amber sail, and a gold rudder and keel, bringing in a load of carbuncles—or if you should say it was the old witch of the ravine come to life, I should about believe you. What do you say, Mr. Stitchkin?"

The tailor stood gazing in dumb bewilderment—when suddenly he clapped his hands and shouted with surprise and delight—

"Why, if it isn't—no, it can't be—yes, it must be—it is—it is Hammawhaxo, or else his ghost! Don't you see him—don't you remember him?"

"No!" cried Nabbum, "do tell—you don't say so—I-I-I sw—an!"

"Let's hail him," they cried, "perhaps he don't see us. Sloop ahoy!" and an answering shout was sent back from the vessel. They ran to the edge of the beach, and very soon the little vessel put directly in for the shore, and Hammawhaxo jumped out; and he and the tailor, who probably had scarcely ever even shaken hands before, rushed into each other's arms.

When the first greetings were over, the carpenter made hasty inquiries about the other dwarfs. When he heard the sad news that they had all either died or been lost, his countenance became much troubled, and the tears stood in his eyes. "Ah," he said, "it is my fault, my miserable weakness. Why did I ever betray the good giant—how could I ever league myself with that cursed—no, I won't curse him—he is punished enough, poor fellow! And I, my friends—will you believe it?—I am a changed man. Suffering, grief, remorse I have had. I am not what I was. But let me tell you my story.

"But, first of all, forgive me, my good Stitchkin, if I have ever said or done any thing to injure you."

"You never have," said the tailor, much affected.

"I don't know," said the carpenter, "I may have done so—I was a miserable, weak, selfish wretch. I am changed. I hope to live to do some good yet."

Hammawhaxo then told them how he had sailed away in search of the wonderful shell-fish, according to agreement with Kobboltozo. But it was partly, he said, because he liked the pleasure of sailing—for he did not much believe in Kobboltozo's fancies. He told how he went to sea with a fair wind, and sailed a good many leagues to the north—how a storm came up and upset his vessel, how his wife and his companions were drowned, and how he escaped by swimming, and reached an island, which he found inhabited by a race of civilized and cultivated people—how he lived among them—how he had thought over his past life, and had determined to be a better and a more useful man—how, at last, he began to long to return to his own island, and to do some good among his people. "So I bought me yonder little sloop," he said, "and bidding these good people adieu, sailed for our island. God grant that I am not too late, for I cannot but think we shall find again some of our missing companions."

14
The Fate of Kobboltozo

"And now you must hear the strangest part of my narrative," said the carpenter. "It relates to Kobboltozo. As I drew near our island, the wind took me to a part of it where I had never been, and I was obliged to moor my little bark under some steep rocks. There I found one of those caves, of which our island seems to be so full, and far in its deepest recesses I saw—what remains of Kobboltozo."

"Is he dead, then?" they asked.

"No—on the contrary he is living in a state of the most perfect contentment with himself and every thing else. He has found at last, he thinks, the giant's shell-fish. And a wonderful shell-fish indeed it must be—though its effects are rather different from what might be expected. Kobboltozo lives in that dim cave, and does nothing but eat oysters and smile at his reflection in the water, and strut up and down like a peacock—for he imagines that he is growing larger and handsomer every day. But the wonderful part of it is that, really, instead of getting hold of the genuine article, he feeds on something possessing just the opposite quality. He is in reality growing rapidly smaller and more disproportioned, instead of larger and shapelier. His head remains its original size, while his legs seem to be dwindling to mere spider's legs!

"And what do you think he was doing when I first discovered him? He was standing on a huge pyramid of empty oyster shells, in the attitude of some mighty sultan, with the whole world beneath him as his obedient slave, and soliloquizing in this way:—'Having risen to these magnificent heights of power, I shall grow to still greater. This island shall be subject to our will. But this island shall be no more than our footstool; our power shall extend to other lands—a world of serfs shall do us reverence. We shall'——

"Here," said Hammawhaxo, "his majesty, the cobbler, discovered me, and recognized his old comrade. 'Hah!' he cried, 'this low-born slave, this son of the hammer and saw! we knew him once, methinks—he shall be our grand vizier, our minister of state, for the fellow has been serviceable to me. Approach, carpenter, and receive the honor we intend for thee!'

" 'Come, old Kobb,' said I, 'leave these ridiculous airs—you are no more a king than I am. Come down from that pile of oyster shells, and take your hat and come with me. Leave this dark cavern, where you have no companions but bats, water-rats, and sea-birds, and let's go back to our village.'

" '*Your* village, not mine,' said Kobboltozo, 'no miserable dwarfs for me—let them perish—let them waste away with fevers—let them kill one another—let them lose themselves in caves and holes of the earth. What care I! We will invoke the gnomes or the mermen, and they will bring us a ship—we will invade other countries, and bring back their nobles and their fair women captives, and found a new government here'——

"He was going on in this strain, when I again interrupted him, by proposing that he should come with me; that I had a vessel all ready.

"He shook his head and smiled, and looked at me with majestic contempt. 'Some day,' he said, 'we shall come, and you will recognize us as your giant king—for the present, it pleases our sovereign will to remain here!'

"Finding it useless to reason with him, I was obliged to abandon him to his fate.

"So there the infatuated fellow remains, eating his oysters, and dwindling away to a mere insect. In a year from this time, I calculate that he will be just about the size of a pin's head."

15

A Beginning and an Ending

Stitchkin was mistaken in imagining that so many of the dwarfs had been lost or had perished. There was quite a number of them, both men and women, who had lost their way, while seeking after the giant's shell-fish, and had come out in another part of the island. They proved to be more rational than many of the others, and kept together, forming a little association, which got along tolerably well. They found a quite beautiful and fertile spot near the southern shore, which they had cultivated; and they succeeded so well that they gradually abandoned the idea of becoming giants, and built up a little settlement, where they devoted themselves to farming, fishing, and the trades to which they had been accustomed. They found this spot better situated, being nearer the sea than the village they had abandoned, which was some way inland, and the soil of which was full of rocks and stones.

This little settlement was discovered one day by Hammawhaxo and Stitchkin, as they were sailing in the carpenter's little vessel round the island. The dwarfs were delighted to see their old acquaintances, and the carpenter and tailor no less so to find so many of their tribe left alive and flourishing.

So they determined to come and settle down there too. The tailor's kindness to those who had suffered, had softened many hearts towards him; and Hammawhaxo, who during his absence had acquired a good deal of useful knowledge, made himself very serviceable to the little community. First, he drew a map of the island, then he discovered a path (made formerly by the giants) leading from the new settlement to the old village, and the dwarfs visited the latter place and brought away all the timber, furniture, tools, cooking utensils, and whatever else they could make use of, to add to and improve their new village. Hammawhaxo showed that he had a wise head and a good heart, as well as an able hand. By his teachings and by his example he was of great benefit. He labored hard to build and adorn their houses—he instructed them and their children in many useful arts—with the assistance of the American sailors, he built boats and fishing vessels—in fine, he was constantly helping others, and teaching them to help themselves. A spirit of industry, contentment, and mutual good will seemed to pervade the little village. Things were going on so well, that when Mr. Nabbum and Jacky left, they felt no anxiety about their future success.

After a stay of several months, during which time Mr. Nabbum had ample opportunity to make many valuable acquisitions to the great Huggermugger Museum he has since established in America, they bid an affectionate farewell to the carpenter and tailor, and promising to visit them again, if ever they made another voyage in those seas, they sailed homeward, and reached the United States in health and safety.

16

Mr. Nabbum's Museum

CONCLUSION

One evening I was sitting alone in my study, thinking what sort of a story I should write for my young friends' next Christmas present. I scratched my head, and bit my pen, and poked the fire, and looked into it—then I stood up and gave myself a good warming—then I sat down with my head on my hand, and a blank quire of paper before me—then I took my pen and began to scribble imps—then I became very sleepy—when there was a knock at my door, and to my great surprise in came Jacky Cable. I didn't know him at first, with his bronzed face, his great beard, and his broad shoulders. He had just arrived from the East Indies, and from Huggermugger's Island. So, after a hearty greeting and a warm welcome, he took a chair by my fire, where he sat steadily talking and telling stories till—will you believe it?—two o'clock in the morning.

So I decided to make a book out of what he told me—and here you have it.

But I have one thing more to tell. I thought I had got through with my story, and the other day was just writing the last page, when Mr. Zebedee Nabbum came stalking in in a state of great excitement.

"If you are reelly goin' to make a book out of what Jacky's told you," said he, "don't do it—till you've seen my museum—because I want you to bring it in somehow."

"Dear me," I said, "I have just got through. I'm afraid it's too late. My story is all written, and must go to be printed."

"No, it aint too late," said Zebedee; "you can *tech in* a leetle here and there, like—you know—jest as a kind of seasonin' or sharp *sarce*, to give it a flavor—can't you? Why, you'd ought to see my museum, reelly. Jacky told you about it, didn't he?"

I said, "Yes, Jacky mentioned that you intended to set up a museum, a great deal better than Barnum's, and had brought home many curious things from the giant's island."

"*Haint* I though!" said Nabbum. "Why you can't do the subject jestice, till you've seen the things I've got. You must come and see. It dooz beat all nater. Why the few privileged persons that's seen it *do* say that it's no mistake—the most remarkable collection of nateral curiosities that was ever got up in the States."

I promised Mr. Nabbum that I would certainly give him a call—but repeated that I was now writing the last chapter of my book, and didn't wish to clog the story with any superfluous details, and "besides," I said, "your museum will be so well known before my book is out, that my notice of it will be useless."

"Well," said Zebedee, "won't you jest run your eye over this list of articles, and bring in some of 'em at the end of your story."

So saying, he handed me a piece of paper, a good deal worn by being carried in the pocket, with some writing on it in pencil.

"They aint all from the giant's island, the things I've put into the Huggermugger Museum," said Zebedee, "but you'll see that some of 'em are."

So I took the list and read it over, and here is an extract from it:—

Three mammoth Pumpkins, with hair growing on them; each measuring——feet diameter, and weighing——tons. (The figures are not legible.)

One Bullfrog Skin; brilliant green; 6 × 4 feet.

Six splendid gigantic Conch Shells. (Figures effaced, but probably of preposterous dimensions.)

One Saucepan—about the size of a large wash-tub—from the giant's house.

One pair Giant's Boots.

Mrs. Huggermugger's Thimble, Scissors, &c.

One Bottle, with the Cork that killed forty dwarfs.

One rare Bird, stuffed, of stupendous size; commonly called the Black-Tooter, or Pulpit-Bird. It had a remarkably loud voice.

One specimen of the Musical Crab, found on the shores of Cape Horn.

One curious specimen of Crinoline Petticoat, supposed, from its extraordinary diameter, to have been worn by a giantess.

A winged White Bear, from Iceland. This singular creature was caught on Mount Hecla, where a flock of them were seen fluttering around the burning crater of the volcano, like moths around a candle.

A Salamander. This animal was also caught on Mount Hecla. The end of his tail was seen sticking out of the crater. It took fifty Norwegian sailors to capture him.

A Sea Serpent, larger than any yet seen. This animal had swallowed a meeting-house on Cape Cod, and died of indigestion.

A Daguerreotype of the Emperor of Japan, and a Model of the last Earthquake in that island.

One petrified Monkey.

Two Ducks, born without legs.

One very remarkable Centipede, with eyes in its tail.

One dried Mannikin, preserved in spirits; supposed by Z. N. to be Kobboltozo.

And so on, and so on.

"Well, Mr. Nabbum," I said, after I had ran over the list, "since you have done me such a service in furnishing so much of the material of my story, I will publish the account of our conversation, and a list of some of these wonderful curiosities."

And now I say to all my young readers, after you have read my story, go and see the Huggermugger Museum—if you can find it.

The Legend of Doctor Theophilus; or, The Enchanted Clothes

1

The Doctor's arrival in Toppledown

Everybody I think knows Fog-land—and its capital city Templedome, or as it has been called in modern days Toppledown. Everybody knows the Fog-land and Toppledown of today, and has doubtless heard of the wonderful changes time has brought about in its climate, in its inhabitants, and in nearly all their customs, laws, institutions. But few perhaps know much about this island and their city as they were some centuries ago. Fewer still I think have heard the story I am about to tell them, the Legend of Doctor Theophilus, the great reformer of the earlier times of Fog-land.

The early history of this island and this city is veiled in much obscurity. It is said that for some hundreds of years such a dense mist brooded over the place, that its existence was but vaguely known, even to the inhabitants of the group of islands of which it forms one in the great Clisonian Archipelago. At the present day, however, as we all know, it is visited by ships from all quarters of the civilized globe.

But there was a time when, had any vessel from another land approached the coast of Fog-land, and ventured into the ports of Toppledown, its advent would have been as strange as that of the ships of Columbus on the shores of Hispaniola.

It is difficult to give a very clear account of this singular country, as it was in the olden days. Things have changed there, to such a degree, that most of the early records are lost or obscured, so that the modern Fog-landers and Toppledownites have perhaps been tempted to imagine and to exaggerate, and embellish in revising the legends of their past history.

It is possible, therefore, that the story I am about to tell may have only a slight foundation of truth. Or it may be, that the original narrator may have intended a hidden meaning therein. So I give it as I heard it—from one of the learned archeologists of the island.

My learned friend informs me that, according to tradition, this Fog-land (which I presume is only an Anglicized name for a word somewhat resembling it in pronunciation) was said to have been really a land of fogs. The capital city Toppledown or Templedome (for the original word is somewhat like both these Anglicized versions) was enveloped in such obscurity that, from having lived so many years without clean sunshine, the people of ancient Toppledown were distinguished for many strange ocular peculiarities. Some were very near-sighted, some squinted, some had the axis of vision distorted away from the facial bridge, some were weak-eyed, some blear-eyed, and many (it is said) had merely rudimentary eyes, like the fishes in Mammoth Cave. In short, the defects of vision were so various, they would have crazed any modern oculist, even to make a catalogue of them. But what was remarkable, none of these poor benighted individuals seemed to be conscious of his or her peculiar defects. All were content with and many—the majority—seemed even proud of their optical organs. My learned friend thinks this ocular condition is really founded in fact.

But a still more notable peculiarity of the Fog-landers was—says my learned Islander—that their mental and often moral vision corresponded to their physical vision. In their foggy condition, they were necessarily Foggies, or old (as we often spell the word) fogies. Seeing things about them so dimly, they naturally fell back on Antiquity, and put more faith in the Old than the New. To them the Old was good *because* it was old. They swore by Methusaleh, the oldest man. They hated to have any old fixtures disturbed, no matter whether they were worm-eaten and rotten or not. They were at once skeptical and superstitious. That any institution was sanctioned by long usage was sufficient to stamp it as eternally true. They must have been related to the Chinese. A cracked jug would have been imitated forever and ever in their pottery—till the flaw became a beauty. If a Toppledownite philosopher had taught, three hundred years before, that two and two in a certain Pickwickian sense make six, or had written a book to prove that a circle was a square, with a slight adaptation to circumstances, quoting the venerable Methusaleh in supporting his creed, woe to the heretic who should contradict it. If a man should ascend one of their little hills, and get above the fog, and declare that the sun sometimes shone all day, without a cloud, and that it would be better for Toppledown to have a little more sunshine or a little less fog, woe to that rash and dangerous free-thinker. Happy for him if he escaped the dungeon or the stake. Just as when there is a grave typographical error committed by means of a little printer's devil, it must run through the 150,000 copies, and never get altered in any future edition, till someone wiser gets into the printing office and rectifies it—so when any bigger devil set a lie going in Toppledown, it ran its course through uncounted years, and even got stereotyped into a seeming truth, till some wiser head corrected the error, by substituting *the true word* for the false.

Someone may say Toppledown couldn't help itself, couldn't drive off the fog, couldn't if it tried see any better than it did. But my learned friend thinks that more than half the obscurity in which these people lived was smoke and miasmatic vapor of their own making—came in fact from their stagnant fens, and from their stupid burnt sacrifices to their idols and demigods. There may be some truth in my friend's theory.

Toppledown seems to have been a large city with tall queer mediaeval-looking old houses, looking down out of suspicious-looking towers and loop-holes and small blear-eyed windows into narrow streets and dingy courtyards. Overhanging roofs screened the inhabitants from whatever they had of sunshine—for the sun did shine on them, faintly, once in a while, in spite of all their efforts to keep dark. A curious old city it was—more quaint I daresay than picturesque. A portion of it lay close to an inlet from the sea. There were a few wharves, and beside these lay a few old decayed-looking vessels somewhat after the Chinese junk model, whose only traffic was around their own coasts, for they seldom ventured out of sight of land.

One night the inhabitants collected together in crowds on the landings and in groups at their windows, attracted by an unusual appearance in the east. It seemed to be a star or comet of considerable magnitude, which nobody had ever noticed before. It was of course veiled in the mist, but was still bright enough to draw their attention. The crowd stood looking at it out of their dim eyes for about half an hour, and then dispersed and went to bed, and the next day seemed to have forgotten all about it. But that night, it is said, there came a little vessel into port, and out of it stepped a stranger, who suddenly disappeared in the shadowy streets of the old town. Few noticed his arrival, and nothing was known of him, till some days after. It happened to be an unusually bright day for Fog-land. A crowd had gathered around a man in a sort of plain Pilgrim's dress of some foreign fashion in one of the public squares. He was stopped, and questioned closely as to his name, country, business, and mysterious appearance in Toppledown. To all their questions he very good-naturedly returned answers in the language of Fog-land, which he spoke with a slight foreign accent. He told them that he came from a country far away to the Eastwards, a wonderful and beautiful land where the air was always fine and healthy, where the sun shone with a mild and vivifying radiance, where the laws were just, the government fraternal, the people loved the light and hated darkness, and each one treated his neighbor as a brother or a sister.

But although there was something magnetically attractive and winning in the stranger's tones—and it seemed as though truth and love itself inspired his words—the Toppledownites shook their heads and shrugged their shoulders, and some went away muttering harsh words, while others glared at him with threatening looks and gestures.

"You haven't told us your name yet, Sir Pilgrim," someone said, "and your profession, and your reasons for coming to Toppledown."

"My name is Theophilus," said the stranger. "I am a physician by profession, and I am travelling for the purpose of studying the various diseases and defects of my fellow man, and of curing them, if possible."

His listeners smiled sneeringly, and asked, "What defects and diseases are there to be cured in the great and glorious city of Toppledown?"

Whereupon Theophilus told them that they would all find themselves much better in health of body and mind if they would only adopt some of his ideas with regard to the sanitary condition of the city; that he believed a great deal of the fog under which they were suffering was only smoke and pestilential vapor from the neglected marshes and pools; and that if they would listen to him, he would undertake a mode of treatment which would purify the air and let in the light, and eventually enable them to *see* as well as he, the Doctor, did.

But this speech only made them furious. "Condition of the city"—they cried—"Make changes in Toppledown! Our own smoke and vapor? Let in the light? *See* as well as *be* seen? O the pernicious radical! O the dangerous and daring innovator! O the despiser of the memory of the great Methusaleh! O the mischievous upsetter of all that is venerable and time-hallowed! Verily, we must report this man to the authorities." And off went one detachment from the throng.

Meanwhile, the rest of the crowd still surrounded Theophilus, eager to know more about him.

"But your plans of improvement, Sir Doctor, you haven't told us about *them.* Wherein do they differ from ours? And do you pretend to cure everything? Tell us something about your system."

"My first prescription," said Theophilus, "would be, as I told you, to get rid of your wet marshes and your cesspools, and to purify your sewers and streets. Then, to stop making these perpetual offerings of smoke and incense to your idols, which so befoul your sky."

"The blasphemer! The atheist!" cried another group. "We shall inform the High Priest of the Temple of the Grand Panjandrum of this." And off was another detachment.

"But what about your medicines, my friend? You have told us nothing of them."

"My medicines are wide-known in the land from which I came. They are not given by guess-work; there is no groping in the dark, now trying this, now that, all experiment. They are *specifics.* They go right to the spot, assisting Nature to throw off and get out of its disorders. They are not surface-cures, like—"

The Doctor paused. His zeal perhaps was carrying him too far for a beginning.

"Like what!" they cried. "Like *ours,* I suppose you mean," cried a pompous-looking citizen with powdered wig and gold chain. "I tell you what, Mr. Quack, we are not going to tolerate any of your newfangled nostrums here. The honorable College of Physicians, of which I have the honor to be the President, will never submit to have anyone who has not graduated within its walls practice medicine here. If you want to cure people, you must cure them in *our* way, according to our rules, or you will find Toppledown a little too hot for you!"

And off went the respectable Professor with his deputation.

A vain-looking little man (whose name sounded something like kitten-lids) with very small weak-looking greenish eyes here stepped forward, and spoke.

"You said something, just now, Signior Doctor, about our not seeing as well as *you* see. I consider that a reflection upon our powers of vision, which you have no right to make. What fault do you find with our eyes, I should like to know?"

The slightest dawning of a smile passed over Theophilus' lips. "My poor friends," he said, "I don't wish to be personal in my remarks upon the optics of any of you, but the truth is, you have lived so long in a fog that you don't know your own defects of vision. I see around me every sort of ocular derangement. I forbear to enter into particulars. You see in the dark, it may be true, but do you wish eyes no better than those of cats, bats, moles, and owls? My friends, I would restore you to your normal powers of vision. You are the victim of a malady our doctors call 'Photophobia.' I only need a little time to cure you all. Come and see me. I shall charge you no fee if you can't afford it, as you will need a little patience, a little thought, a little good will."

But here there was another growling in the crowd, especially in that part most fashionably dressed, and having the most aristocratic *aplomb*. "What is the fellow talking about!" they said. "What impertinence! Come, we've had enough of this. See as well as he does, indeed! Who made you so wise, I should like to know? As if the people of the glorious city of Toppledown were not the handsomest people yet known. Yes, and the keenest-sighted too. Where in the world are there men with such fine large yellow and sea-green eyes? Where women with such pretty little optic beads on each side of their noses! See in the dark! So much the better! How else could we live in our tall, shadowy houses? Or find our way through our cool dark streets? See in the dark! I rather think we can! You, I suppose, would like to have it always broad glaring sunshine, and put our eyes out with your dangerous and foolish light-experiments."

And here marched off the fashionable wing of the crowd, which was now growing thin—only a few of the poorer class lingered behind, more or less interested in the stranger. Two of them stood conversing a little apart.

"The fact is," said one, "if *I* want any physic, I shall go to the old Magician—you know who I mean. He cures you quick—and don't ask a big fee."

"Yes," said a laborer whose name was Godfrey, "but this Theophilus said he didn't take *any* fee from the poor."

"But that's all pretence—take him a good purse of gold at night, or slip money secretly into his hand, and take my word for it, he won't object. Besides, who knows but he may poison you with his new-fashioned drugs."

"I have no fear," said Godfrey. "There is something in him that leads me to put implicit trust in whatever he says or does."

2

What the Owl-Faces said of Him

Doctor Theophilus, it is said, lived in a small house on an obscure street and dressed in plain clothes, and therefore the wealthy and respectable Toppledownites would perhaps never have troubled themselves much about him if he had kept quiet. But it was impossible for him to hide his light under a bushel. He would persist in going about from house to house, among the poor and sick, and even collected people about him in the streets and squares to whom he administered pills and tinctures, prescribing for all their complaints; and at times his house was thronged with patients, who went away proclaiming the wonderful efficacy of his medicines. This began to interfere with the trade of the established doctors, who began to complain loudly, and who intrigued secretly to put him down.

They said, too, that he was discovered one night filling up with earth a stagnant pool that stood in back of his house—a proceeding quite contrary to authority.

One day, two of the respectable owl-faces met in the shadow of an old archway leading into a narrow and dingy street.

"Good day, Mr. Hibou," said Doctor Sangsue. "There's no news I hope. Everything is going on as usual, I trust. I hope the sun has not broken into your house lately. I sometimes find that queer luminary quite troublesome. Unfortunately I have two young students in my family, who have lately taken it into their heads to open the windows—which annoys me a good deal."

"Luckily I'm not much troubled that way," said Hibou. "I have built such thick screens about my windows that it must be an awfully bright day that can do me any damage. I always keep dark and cool."

"You are lucky," said Sangsue. "We doctors, unfortunately, are obliged to go about among our patients, and it's quite dreadful, sometimes, I assure you, the way the sun pierces through the townsmoke. What *was* that mysterious orb of flame made for, I wonder? But tell me, have you heard anything more of this quack Theophilus, who goes about calling himself Doctor?"

"I am sorry to say," replied Hibou, "that I have both seen him and heard of him. Take my word for it, he is a dangerous person. They say the common people are bewitched by him."

"And they don't pretend to say that his drugs do them any good?"

"Any good! I should like you to hear some of the stories I have heard of his miraculous cures."

"Well, well—we must put a stop to this," said Sangsue. "I shall lay this matter before the College of Physicians, at once. It isn't fit that such an adventurer should come, pretending to rank as our equal."

Accordingly, the case was laid before the College of Physicians, all of whom with one accord turned red and pale, like an united brotherhood of turkeycocks, and forthwith passed terrific resolutions against the daring innovator. One of these resolutions was as follows:

"Resolved that Dr. Sangsue, Dr. Musophof, and Dr. Statusquo be appointed a Committee to wait upon said Theophilus, and inform him that it is clearly contrary to the time-honored institutions of the city, and subversive of the cause of Science in Fog-land, that anyone not having graduated from the Toppledown College of Physicians be permitted to practice medicine in the island. And that, at least, the said Theophilus must show a diploma from some other Medical Institute of sufficient note before he has any right to pursue his present course."

The committee accordingly waited on Theophilus, who replied that he had no diploma that they could read, for it was written in invisible ink. Truth, he said, must speak for itself. No certificate could make it more true than it is. He was willing to be tried by the results of his practice.

This answer failed to satisfy the College of Physicians, who forthwith organized a serious opposition to him. They collected all sorts of evidence against him, which made him out to be a curious compound, for it was said that he was

A foreigner
A meddler
A spy
A secret plotter against Fog-land
A fool
A crazy man

A sorcerer
A rich miser
A poor spendthrift
Too much of a saint
Too much of a sinner
A perverter of understandings
A corrupter of hearts
A plain speaker
A teller of lies
An innovator
A dangerous experimenter in light
A disturber of pools
A foe to umbrella and screens
A quack
A gratis-doctor
An atheist
Vain
Presumptuous
Un-Toppledownish

But the enmity of the Doctor College was unavailing. Theophilus had done nothing contrary to law, and so far as public opinion went, he had the people with him.

The Mayor of the city was at first disposed to set his face against the new Doctor, but when he found he had grown so popular, he became his friend, and invited him one day to a great dinner. Theophilus didn't care for great dinners. He would rather have dined tête à tête with the Mayor in some quiet little chop-house. But it occurred to him that he might meet with some distinguished citizens whom he might influence toward his system of cures and reforms. So he accepted. After dinner, the conversation took the turn Theophilus wished, and the result was that the Mayor, at least, became even more his friend than before.

3

The Grand Panjandrum

Now it happened that not long after this occurred the annual festival of the Grand Panjandrum.

And who was the Grand Panjandrum?

Was he Emperor, King, Califf, High Priest, Hero? Was he some old demigod? Or some inspired prophet, poet, or sage of ancient times? Not at all. I am told that the Grand Panjandrum had never had a personality of any sort. All that there was of him was there: a huge wooden idol, clothed in silk and silver, and adorned with strange half-pagan emblems, sitting in stupid staring majesty on a throne at the entrance of the Council house. The framework was probably quite ancient. But the robes in which it was clothed were said to have been furnished by a great Magician of Toppledown. The *simulacrum* had been set up a good many years since, and the people had once venerated it as an idol. Even now some of the more superstitious offered sacrifices to it. But the image was getting old and shabby; its glass eyes had tumbled out and the wind whistled through the holes; and there it sat for no better reason than because their ancestors had placed it there and had venerated it. Still, it was customary to observe a fête day in its honor, and on that day it was a sort of religious form, for everyone passing, to take off his cap to the huge figure—which is said to have sometimes nodded in return—and this recognition was considered by many a good omen.

Now Theophilus, happening to be in the crowd who were doffing their caps, not only did not take off his hat, but stood and laughed outright at the stupid old lay-figure. Some of the priests and doctors noticed it, and lost no time in proclaiming everywhere that Theophilus was an atheist, or he would not have treated their time-honored institution in that irreverent way. By great efforts they succeeded in working on the prejudices of many of the more ignorant and superstitious, until a strong party was formed against him. By a skilful use of their testimony, his enemies prevailed upon the Council—though the Mayor did his best to prevent it—to arrest him and send him to prison. They then excited an aristocratic mob to pull his house down; and a great search was made for his medicine chest, but they couldn't find it, for Theophilus had been warned by some friends to conceal it. The court then assembled and the Doctor was brought in to be tried. His accusers brought against him a mass of false and exaggerated testimony. But they found it impossible to make out a case, for he had a host of witnesses in his favor. After the court had sat several days without being able to come to a decision, the Chief Judge, at last, reviewing some old law nearly obsolete, decided that they should bring the prisoner, the lawyers, and the witnesses all before the Grand Panjandrum, and if the figure nodded its head, when asked if the prisoner were guilty, he should be condemned to death; if not, he should be released. So Theophilus was taken to the front of the Council House. The people all crowded around in breathless suspense, and the Judge stood up and said: "O grand Panjandrum, if this man be guilty of the charges brought against him, be graciously pleased to bow thy august head."

The crowd did not wait long in suspense. To the great surprise and horror of the friends of Theophilus, the figure did actually bow its head! Then the Judge turned to the people and said: "Ye see, O Men of Toppledown, that the great Panjandrum bows his godlike head. The man must die." And the guards came forward to seize the prisoner and hurry him away.

But the Mayor of the city, who was neither a believer in the Panjandrum nor in the incorruptibility of the Judge, was determined, if possible, to save his new friend. This worthy functionary, who in addition to a good pair of eyes—a gift which interfered somewhat with his popularity—usually carried in his pocket a small spy-glass, which served him in detecting many a transgression. On this occasion, he had taken his station on a platform on the other side of the Square, facing the Council House, directly in front of the figure, and was now peering at its head with all his might through his glass, when he became sure that he discovered the hands of a man through the holes where the glass eyes had been. Instantly the monstrous puzzle rose before him as clear as day.

"My lord Chief Justice," said the Mayor, stepping forward and waving his staff of office to enforce attention. "One word, if you please. By virtue of my authority I have a right to stay sentence on the prisoner, provided further proof can be furnished in his favor. I now undertake to show to this assembled crowd that they have been deceived by a shameful trick—in fact that there is a man now concealed in the head of that figure."

"It is impossible!" cried the Judge, who, however, turned as pale as death. And he rushed toward the figure and, as the Mayor thought, made use of secret signs to warn the wretch within of approaching danger. But it was too late, for the crowd had caught the intimation of the fraud and came swarming around the image, where, by lifting a fold of its robes, they discovered a door large enough to admit a man. This they tore open, and a narrow stair was seen heading to the head, which was hollow and large enough to receive the body of a man. It wasn't an empty head this time, however, for there was the Head-Mover, waiting for the dispersion of the crowd, before he should descend. It was not necessary for him to wait, for he was dragged down into the square in the sight of all Toppledown. This furious populace was for tearing the miserable wretch in pieces, but the Mayor interfered and commanded that he should be taken to prison. Then turning to the iniquitous Judge, he said: "My lord Chief Justice, I should not have suspected you of being an accomplice in this atrocious conspiracy against the life of an innocent man. Now I must do my duty. Seize him, guards, and carry him too to prison."

The Mayor then ordered a street search for all persons concerned in this wicked plot. In the meantime, the excited populace, no longer showing any veneration for the Panjandrum, had commenced the process of demolition. First they tore off the robes, then an arm, then a leg; then they battered down the huge trunk and broke it in pieces and, dragging the fragments into the square, they burnt them with shouting and laughter.

Strangely enough, the Panjandrum robes had disappeared and could nowhere be found. The Magician, it is said, who furnished them, had been present in the crowd, and had contrived in the confusion to carry them off. And hurrying to his house, locked them up in an iron chest.

4

The Doctor's affairs prosper

Things now took a decided turn in Doctor Theophilus' favor. His enemies were powerless to harm him. And day by day he became more popular with all classes.

In a few years, nearly every individual in Toppledown became his friend or well-wisher. He had cured so many men, women, and children; he had introduced such excellent sanitary reforms; he had been the means of removing so many old prejudices and superstitions; he had by his example so improved the morals and manners, and kindly dispositions of the people, that his reputation had become firmly established throughout all Fog-land. He was becoming a rich man. He lived in a large, handsome house. He had servants in livery at his doors. He fared daintily, and gave and accepted fine entertainment. But his prosperity did not harden his heart, nor enervate his energies, in the reform he had commenced, nor diminish his zeal in the dissemination of his views.

Having now a very large practice, Doctor Theophilus took several students under his roof, who imbibed his spirit and worked with him and relieved him of the anxiety of seeing after such a crowd of patients. Seeing affairs going on so well, he yielded a little to an old love of meditation and study, and devoted a large part of his time to books and mystical abstraction from the world. He lived an unmarried life, and became more and more possessed with the idea that it was best he should be a bachelor, as the care of a wife and children would have interfered too much with his prayers and meditations, as well as with his active duties.

But though the Doctor passed a good deal of his time in retirement from the world, it must be confessed that he had one little weakness at this period of his career. He had known poverty and obscurity and persecution. He had struggled bravely through all his trouble, encouraged by the belief that his system was the right one and would prevail. But now that he was growing wealthy and influential, he said to himself: "I see that my fine house and furniture, my students, and my servants are doing a good deal to strengthen my hands and add to my influence. But here am I still dressed no better than the people about me. This will hardly do. It doesn't become a man who has attained my position and who feels his superiority, as I can't help feeling mine, to dress in an ordinary style. My apparel should suit my character and place. I shall be honored and respected all the more, by appearing before the people well-dressed."

Accordingly Theophilus began to go abroad arrayed in silks and velvets, in ermine and embroidery, and laces of silver and gold. And he certainly did create a sensation. What a charm there is in dress! And what an influence too! An ill-dressed person is like a lute out of tune. When we have once felt the harmony that exists between ourselves and our clothing, we never wish to relapse into the sartorial discords that our poverty has so long perpetuated.

People now stopped and inquired who that grand dignified handsome gentleman was. "What, don't you know Doctor Theophilus—the great, the good Doctor?" "Not Doctor Theophilus! Well, I declare! I should hardly have known him!" He was charmed with the effect he produced. Everyone now took off his hat to him. Everyone turned to gaze after him. The Doctor didn't sufficiently reflect how much of this respect was paid to his new hat and feather, his ermine robe, or his diamond ring.

By degrees this regard for dress grew with a love of finery and display. His holiday suits became quite gorgeous. He was tempted quite often to show himself in public—on the promenades, and even at gay festivals and masquerades. But this taste for fine display alternated with his habits of retirement and meditation. Often after a night of masquerading, he would steal back to his books and forget all about the gay world.

For Theophilus had two sides to him—an outer side for the world, an inner side for his friends, his patients, and his hours of communion with himself.

5

The Magnetic Clothes

It was Carnival week (for it seems the Christian Saturnalia were observed even in Fog-land) and Doctor Theophilus was passing through a dark narrow street chiefly occupied by clothes-dealers and costume shops. At the doors and windows hung all sorts of Masquerading robes, new and old, plain and fantastic, of any style and color. There were costumes of all nations. There were dominoes of all hues. There were masks of every sort—respectable and grotesque.

The Doctor sauntered along, looking now at this shop, now at that, but apparently unable to find what he wanted. At last at the end of the street, he was accosted by a strange-looking old man, who stood at his shop door, and with a smile invited him to enter, saying that he was an artist in dress and knew exactly what his excellency wanted. Moreover, he was quite sure he had the very thing of all others that would suit and fit him. Theophilus entered and the old man eagerly overhauled his dresses, until appearing to think a moment, he went into a back room and brought out a suit, apparently new, but made up of somewhat-faded silk and velvet. "This, now I think of it," said the clothes-dealer, "seems to me will fit you exactly. Be so good as to try it on." The Doctor did so, and found that the suit fitted him admirably. It was somewhat fantastically designed, but picturesque and becoming to his figure. The subdued tints of the stuff, also, rather pleased his taste, for he was somewhat weary of very bright and gay colors. He accordingly purchased it, and had it sent immediately to his house.

That night he wore his new suit at a ball. He was so charmed with the clothes—their style and excellent fit—that he thought he should like to wear them not only at festivals, but every day. For somehow this suit seemed to communicate to his limbs a freedom and elasticity he had never felt before. When he took one step, he seemed to accomplish at least two. When he raised his arm, it flew up without an effort. When he took off his hat to salute an acquaintance, it would describe the graceful arc of a circle in his hand without his intention. He was conscious of a greater grace in all his movements. He arrived at the great theatre where the ball was given. When he entered, he seemed to be buoyed up and whirled about by an excess of animal spirits. He floated up and down the room, as if walking the air in a dream. He threaded his way through the crowd with incredible swiftness and ease. His unusual liveliness was remarked, as strongly contrasting with his generally grave and dignified deportment. But when his friends finally saw the Doctor dancing—yes actually dancing—they stood amazed, and suspected him to be under the influence of some of his own magical drugs. There he was in the gay ring of the girls and harlequins, enjoying himself like a youth of eighteen, dancing as if his life depended upon it. And he danced on till the night wore away, and the music stopped from sheer exhaustion, and the crowd thinned off, and daylight made the candles dim. He was among the last to leave the festive hall. As he returned, he thought he should be a good deal fatigued on awaking, and so he was, until he put on the carnival suit again, just to see how he looked by daylight, when he instantly felt refreshed again.

"This is wonderful," he said. "There must be some peculiar magnetic quality about this suit of clothes, for I feel no fatigue whatever. I am as light and elastic as a boy. How fortunate to come into their possession! I can now sit up all night and study. I can do without sleep, and by so much time gained, enlarge my sphere of usefulness. On the whole, I think I must wear this suit every day, fantastic as it may seem."

So Doctor Theophilus wore his wonderful suit down to breakfast, astonishing his servants and students. He even wore it in the streets, astonishing the respectable people of Toppledown still more. And when asked by one of his friends why he took such a fancy to it, he answered, as he really thought, that it possessed a remarkable electric or magnetic virtue, which took away all fatigue and depression of spirits; that he had never had a suit that fitted him as this did; and that as to its not being exactly in the fashion, he hoped it would be ere long.

And it *did* get to be the fashion soon, so great was the Doctor's influence even in this line. But nobody could find or get made a suit having precisely the cut of it, still less possessing its wonderfully magnetic virtue. Many went to the old costume vender's shop hoping to get suited, but it was all in vain. The old man had nothing resembling it and professed to be quite ignorant that there was anything peculiar about it.

This suit had certainly some very desirable qualities, but in a little while it proved to be quite the reverse, in some respects. Sometimes it seemed to communicate to its wearer an excess of action (which was not always convenient) and sometimes it acted as a clog and fetter. It would lead the wearer to do things he never intended to do, and it prevented him from doing what he *did* intend. If he only raised his hand to touch his hat to a friend, he was somehow induced to take it off three times, with a great flourish. If he raised a glass of wine to his lips, he was compelled to drink it off and bring the goblet down on the table with a clatter. If he wished to walk slowly, he was hurried up in an unaccountable way; or if he would stop quickly to see a sick patient, his legs would become paralyzed as in a nightmare. He would sometimes trip in his speech and make verbal blunders, or say very extravagant things. Then again the clothes would stiffen and weigh upon him. If he knelt down to say his prayers, he would find it hard to get up. If he wished to give alms to a beggar, he couldn't find his pockets, or if he did, he couldn't find his purse. Sometimes when undressing the stuff would become stiff as buckram and seemed glued to his limbs, and at another time, when dressing, it would fly off at tangents, and to get his arm into the left-hand sleeve was a feat nothing short of legerdemain could accomplish.

You may imagine that such *tantrums* in a suit of clothes were annoying and quite inexplicable. But whether the Doctor got used to the clothes or the clothes to the Doctor, these eccentricities became less and less frequent.

Well, the legend says that he continued to wear them for a long time—how long it does not say—till at last they began to grow somewhat old and tarnished, and the Doctor wore them less frequently. But he noticed that whenever, after having left them off for a while, he put them on again, they *acted* worse than ever—as if in revenge for being neglected. They would wrinkle and pucker and hitch up and hitch down, as if any old one were in them, till the Doctor concluded to lay them aside entirely, and adopted a plainer suit, especially when visiting his patients, or when at home in his study, when he would slip into an easy dressing gown and busy himself in his books and meditations.

6

The Clothes without the Doctor

One would think that any old suit of clothes, if it had a soul, would be heartily rejoiced to be laid aside and have a little rest and retirement. Strange to say, this was not the case with these singular garments of Doctor Theophilus.

The legend here verges on the fantastically puerile, but I must follow it and not invent. It declares that there was a kind of a *quasi* soul in the garments—or if not a soul, a susceptibility to magic or mesmerism, or some mysterious power which put a tricky spirit into them, thereby distinguishing them from all other sartorial integuments ever contrived by tailors or tailoresses. In our day, when "spiritual manifestations" are as common as a quotation of stocks, the properties I have described as belonging to these magic garments may not seem purely imaginary.

When this suit of clothes found itself neglected, it began to grow nervous and fidgety, and twitched itself about in the closet, and wrinkled and puckered, and looked very melancholy, and at last said to itself that it couldn't stand this treatment any longer, but must go out, as it had been accustomed.

One evening a neighbor of the Doctor called in, and the conversation being upon the enchanted clothes—whose peculiarities the Doctor had been describing—his friend ventured to declare a suspicion which had come into his mind—which was now assuming certainty—that this queer suit was made of the silk and velvet robes that had been worn by the Grand Panjandrum—that being a dealer in silks and velvets, he had observed the remarkable resemblance between the pattern of the Doctor's robes and those he recollected as having adorned the idol. Further, he believed that this old clothes-dealer who had sold the suit was no other than the Magician who had clothed that image, but when it was being destroyed by the mob, the old man had secreted the stuff, and had wrought out of it a suit expressly for him, Doctor Theophilus—"for you may be assured," said his friend, "this old man is your bitter enemy, for he is related to the unjust Judge who would have condemned you to death."

The Doctor listened attentively to his friend's story, and said there might be something in it, and he would be on the look for further disclosures.

Meanwhile, as I was saying, the suit of clothes seemed to be possessed with a spirit, for it stretched out first one flabby arm, then another, then its flabby and empty legs, then wriggled toward the Doctor's hat and shoes, and after several attempts succeeded in rolling itself up into a bundle. The bundle then rolled itself along, reached an open door, and flopped off to the old clothes-dealer's shop. The Doctor had dropped asleep in his armchair at the time and knew nothing about it.

The Magician (who, as you see, was the old clothes-dealer) was pleased, but not much surprised to see the bundle bounce into his shop door.

"Welcome, at last, good Bundle," he said. "You have obeyed my summons. I saw you didn't like being neglected by your wearer. Now, since the Doctor thinks he can do without you, how would you like to do without the Doctor? You shall do so, if you like. We'll make a man of you yet. There, take heart! Don't look so flabby and downcast! Puff up a little! Shake your legs—stand up! What, you can't stand up yet without that foolish fellow inside of you? Well, I must use some strong conjuration. Then I must stuff you and put your mask on, for I have painted one so like the Doctor that it will deceive everybody. There I see you have brought his hat and shoes with you. That was clever. That shows something like life and thought in you. Now let's see you on your legs. There—I've stuffed you, so you *must* stand. Now for the mask. Now the hat and feather. Ha, ha! Why, you'd deceive the Professor of Anatomy of the College of Physicians himself. Ah, if we could only make you talk. But that's beyond my power. You will always be a Dummy. But no matter, we'll wrap a shawl around your mouth and tell the people that the Doctor has the *bronchitis*, and must not open his mouth in the night air, for it is chiefly at night that I depend on your going about in the character of Theophilus. But it will require all my magic to make you walk."

So the old Magician mesmerized the Dummy, until he not only stood, but moved. He saturated him, so to speak, with his potent enchantments. Then he took him out in the dead of night and walked him up and down the streets, till he felt sure he could go unattended.

"But it won't do for Theophilus to miss his clothes too long," said the Magician, "or he will suspect something, so you must return before morning to your house. I call it *your* house, for I mean that you shall be master of it in course of time. So when you have done acting your part, come to me and I will take out your stuffing and send you home. I am delighted, my dear Dummy, with the progress you have made under my instruction."

7

The Dummy at Work

The enchanted clothes had now become so much of a personality that it will become necessary to call them "he," and accept the Magician's name "Dummy." Dummy was soon so far advanced that he began to go out by the volition of the old Wizard, and might be seen gliding about the streets every night. He acted the Doctor's part very creditably for a lay figure. We all know how a man's hat and coat come to look like the wearer. Then the mask was a good likeness of the original, and the Doctor's figure and gait were well enough imitated to deceive at night the people, whose deficits of vision I have already commented upon.

But it grieved the good people to see that the Doctor appeared rather pale and sick, and that he kept his hat over his eyes and his mouth muffled, as if afraid of the night air and fog. It was murmured, too, that he had lost his voice. "Poor man!" they said, "It is all owing to his self-sacrificing devotion to his patients. There must be a good many sick. He is out every night, so late. We all are sure he must have some secret grippe. See how he pulls his hat over his eyes, as if to avoid notice."

"I'll call tomorrow morning," said a kind neighbor of the Doctor's, "to see how he is." And the next morning, while the Doctor was sitting in his study, the kind neighbor came in.

"Oh, my dear sir," he said, "what an unwearied worker you are! How is your throat today? I was told it was the *bronchitis*—but I hope not very serious?"

"My good friend," said the Doctor, "I don't know what you mean. I haven't the slightest trouble of the sort. I never was in better health."

His visitor was glad to be correctly informed and, apologizing for the interruption, took his leave.

All this while Dummy, in his original flabby condition, lay in the next room, listening to the conversation—and actually laughed, but it was in his *sleeve*.

At night Dummy was off again to the Magician, who having duly prepared him, set him on his legs and sent him into the streets.

As Dummy was turning a corner, he met Godfrey, a farm laborer who was mentioned as one of the Doctor's early converts. He seemed to be in deep distress, but his face lit up the moment he caught sight of the Doctor's hat and coat.

"Oh dear Sir, I was just hurrying to your house. My wife has been taken very ill—do come at once to see her!"

Dummy seemed to consider for a moment, and then accompanied the man. They passed through several obscure alleys and entered a miserable old house, ascended a creaking staircase, and entered the poor man's rooms. His wife lay ill on her bed. The false Doctor did nothing but look with his glass eyes on the patient, took out of his pocket some pills of lime in sawdust, which he placed on the woman's tongue, and turned to depart.

They wondered he did not speak. He only pointed to his muffled throat, then made another sign intimating that he must have his fee.

"A fee, Doctor?" said Godfrey. "Ah, I know I owe you many and many a sum of gold for the good you have done me and mine at other times. I know it—I never can repay you—but—but—I really thought—as you never asked a fee of the poor—but, Doctor, if you wish it—I will try to pay you." And the poor man brought out half his week's earnings—a paltry sum—and placed it in the hand of the cold automaton, who thereupon took his leave.

The money thus extorted from the poor laborer seemed to embolden the Dummy to try his hand again. As he was passing a café, he happened to see through the windows one of the Doctor's friends. So he glided in and took a seat near him.

"Ah, Doctor, it is you. Come in to get something warm this chilly evening. I see you keep your shawl around your mouth. Lost your voice, I hear. Come, won't you take something? No, not even a cup of coffee?"

Dummy made signs that he would like to borrow some money. "Of course, my dear Doctor. How much? But I thought you were so rich, you never needed to borrow."

Dummy held up his ten gloved fingers. "Ten? Ten what? Ducats?" Dummy nodded, took the offered money, and hastily moved toward the door.

"What? Going already, Doctor? Won't take anything for your cold? No? Well, good night. You are looking very pale. Do take care of yourself. Bless me, how cold your hand is!"

"Somehow, the Doctor seems very formal tonight," he said as Dummy went out, "I never saw him so stiff before."

The next morning, Doctor Theophilus was at his studies in his library when in came Godfrey, saying that his wife was a great deal worse. Wouldn't he come at once and see her?

"Your wife ill?" said the Doctor. "Why didn't you come for me before?"

"It's only a few hours since you were there," said Godfrey.

"Where?" said the Doctor.

"At my house," said the man.

"I haven't been to your house."

"Is it possible, Doctor, you've forgotten last night, when I met you in the street, and—"

"You met me in the street? Why, I wasn't out last night. What's the meaning of all this?" And the two stood looking at each other in dumb perplexity and thinking the other was out of his wits.

"Come," said the good Doctor, "there's some mistake here. It was somebody else you met. I was not aware I had a *double* in Toppledown. Now run home, my dear fellow, and I will be there in fifteen minutes."

The poor woman was very ill but began soon to recover, after the Doctor's visit.

Godfrey was wondering whether the Doctor would expect his fee, when to his joy and astonishment the benevolent physician opened his purse and placed in the poor man's hand a sum three times as large as that the pretended Doctor had extorted from him.

A day or two after, in came the Doctor's friend whom Dummy had met in the café.

"My dear sir," he said, "I am so sorry to trouble you, but I have unexpectedly a large bill to pay, and I find I haven't quite enough to meet it. If you could, without inconvenience, let me have the little sum I lent you the other night, you would very much oblige me."

"My dear friend," said the Doctor, "I don't remember borrowing any money of you. It must have been someone else. But I shall be glad to lend you some. How much shall it be?"

"But surely, Doctor, you can't have forgotten—Thursday night—wasn't it?—at the Café Mussocaldo—the night your *bronchitis* was so bad. Don't you remember? Now that's a good joke. You couldn't talk—kept your mouth muffled in a shawl—and made signs that you wanted some money, and held up your ten fingers—and when I said 'Ten Ducats?' you nodded."

"And took the money!" gasped the good man.

"Of course you took it. Why, Doctor, where is your memory?"

"You are sure it was I?" said the Doctor.

"Why yes—I'm sure there's nobody in Toppledown so like you —the very hat and feather and coat were unmistakeable. The only thing was your loss of voice, your paleness, and an uncommon formality which I couldn't account for."

"This is incredible!" faltered the Doctor. "What does it all mean? Bronchitis! That's the second time they've told me I had the *bronchitis*."

"A thought strikes me," said his friend. "Let me ask you a question. Are you a somnambulist?"

"I never heard that I was. I generally sleep very soundly. But I can easily settle that question. Thursday night, you say? At what time was it?"

"About nine o'clock. I remember hearing the town clock strike as you left the café."

"And *I* remember hearing it strike, sitting here in this very chair," said the Doctor. "Clearly I couldn't have been in both places at once."

"This is very extraordinary," said his friend.

"And what is more, I did not step out the whole evening," said the Doctor. "No, I am concerned that some wicked imposter is going about town, and contriving to pass himself off for me. As for the money you need, my dear sir, you are welcome to it and we'll settle this some other time. I must unmask this villain and try to bring him to justice."

But instead of setting about the work of detecting the imposter, Doctor Theophilus sat in his library, absorbed in his studies.

8

Waking up

Several weeks passed and the thought of the Doctor's *double* only crossed his mind as an unpleasant dream, which he shook from him.

But there came fresh inquiries about his sore throat and loss of voice. Then persons came or wrote for explanations why he had not kept appointments he had never made. Bills came for articles he had never purchased, notes of apology for not being able to lend him money he had never asked for. Complaints that his medicines didn't take effect, or that persons had died after having taken them, according to his prescription. And finally rumors reached him through his friends that his reputation as a man of truth and a reliable physician was fast going downhill, and that if he didn't look sharply after his affairs, all Toppledown would consider him an errant quack and dishonest pretender.

Then Theophilus began to wake up a little, and held a consultation with his friends as to what should be done.

The friend who had suggested the idea that the magnetic clothes were made of the Panjandrum's robe, and that the old clothes-dealer was the Magician, reminded him of what he had said and strongly urged him to make a complaint against the said clothes-dealer. But the Doctor saw no clear connection between this story and the unknown person who was assuming his character.

All inquiries about the imposter were fruitless. Police detectives were set upon the search. The Magician kept his Dummy out of the way. The vigilant Mayor used his spy-glass in vain.

At last one of the detectives brought the Doctor word he had seen someone resembling him gliding along the street of the clothes-dealers; that he had immediately pursued him and called upon him to stop, but that the figure went with incredible swiftness, and he had seen him enter the old clothes-dealer's shop, and the door suddenly shut. The policeman knocked, again and again. And finally someone appeared at a window above. It was the old clothes-dealer in his nightcap, who asked in a great rage what the deuce he wanted and why he disturbed honest people's sleep at that late hour. The policeman replied that he was in search of a suspected person, whom he had seen enter his shop. "Come in then, and see for yourself," said the old man, which the detective accordingly did, and searched the whole house, but found no one. The only place of concealment he didn't look into was an iron chest, but that was plainly too small for a man to get into.

It may seem singular that all this time Doctor Theophilus did not miss his magnetic clothes. The truth is, his mind had been so occupied with his books and his patients that he had quite forgotten for the time his strange carnival suit.

One evening, however, he happened to see the neglected clothes in his wardrobe, and took a sudden notion to put them on once more and go out; it was so long since he had worn them.

He had no sooner got into the street than he began to feel very strangely uncomfortable. Coat and vest, doublet and hose—all seemed alive and possessed with a most rebellious spirit. They puckered and wrinkled, behind and before. They pulled this way and that way, and almost lifted him off his legs. He could hardly move his arms. He could hardly breathe. Now a button would burst, now a strap or buckle would start, or something would tear and rip. He seemed to be whirled and bewitched by some diabolic power. He thought of going back to change the clothes for others, but by some unaccountable power he was unable to turn around. Besides he had no time, for he was obliged to keep a punctual appointment.

It is unnecessary to say how the poor Doctor suffered all that evening. When he reached his house, he slipped on his old loose gown and flung the refractory garments impatiently upon the floor of an adjoining room, with a vow that it should be the last time he would ever trouble himself with the detestable trumpery.

When the Dummy—or the essential part of him—was flung aside in this decided way, he began to waltz and flaunt about the room in a state of ridiculous exhilaration. "It is the last time," he thought, "that I shall be the servant of this old goose of a Doctor. I shall serve one greater than he. Indeed, I don't see why I shall not be my own master, and make others serve *me*. I shall go off tonight, and shan't trouble myself much about coming back. The fact is, Doctor Theophilus and myself have not for some time sympathized. It is very natural that I, who am of a practical and conservative turn of mind, and baby to the family of the Grand Panjandrum of cemented memory, should be misunderstood by a fanatical dreamer. So adieu, Doctor. I go now to my Master—my friend and fellow-worker, I mean—and it is not probable we shall meet again." And the clothes waltzed and rustled and flapped about the room.

But tonight the Doctor seemed to have new ears. He heard the whispering and rustling as he sat in his study. He crept to the door and listened, and within heard, or imagined he heard whispered, part of the above soliloquy. Suddenly the truth flashed on him—and yet it seemed so ridiculous that he could hardly refrain from laughing aloud. He restrained himself, however, and as softly as possible opened the door of the chamber. There stood the sham, shaking his flabby legs and arms, and trying to puff himself out, like a young balloon, and to stand and walk. He made several attempts, and after a good deal of wriggling and struggling, he stopped, with a drooping, melancholy look, and rustling out a kind of silken sigh, sank exhausted on the floor.

Theophilus now stepped in, intending to seize his clothes and lock them up in a trunk. But they slipped away from him, as if some-one outside had tied a string to them and whipped them off. Away they flopped out of the window. He rushed to see where they were going, and in the moonlight just caught a glimpse of them rolling and skipping and flopping along, with his hat and shoes, down the street.

In an instant he rushed out after them. But they flew while he only ran, and were soon out of sight. The Doctor, however, knew where they were going, and started off at full speed toward the Old Clothes street. On the way, he met some people who were very much astonished to see the good man, in his dressing gown and slippers, and without a hat, running, puffing, and panting—turning corners, crossing streets, making shortcuts down dark alleys—in pursuit of some invisible fugitive.

"What's the matter?" they asked. "Where are you going?" "The clothes—the clothes—the imposter—the quack—the scoundrel," shouted the Doctor. "Stop thief—stop thief!"

Whereupon they joined him in the chase, though they had not the faintest idea what they were running after, and thought the good man was out of his wits. "Stop thief—stop thief!" still cried the Doctor, making the best use of his legs. At length he drew near the costume-vender's shop, and as he turned a corner, saw the clothes twitched in, and the door slammed shut. The Doctor knocked and banged, but the old Magician determined to be not at home. He was very busy bolstering up his automaton for an escape, and a night's work of imposture. But the Doctor pushed and banged so furiously that the door at last gave way, and in he rushed. The Magician had got Dummy on his legs in a great hurry, and was performing his usual conjuration over him, when the excited Doctor aimed a blow of his fist full at the figure's head, which crushed his fine mask and knocked out one of his false eyes. Without losing a second, with the other fist, he knocked all Dummy's false teeth down his throat. The hat tumbling off, he picked it up and set it firmly on his own head, where it belonged.

The Magician, who seemed to be prepared, now seized a red-hot poker, and with his eyes flashing fire and a horrible grin on his wrinkled old face, rushed upon his adversary. But the Doctor adroitly stepped aside, and pulling a Bible out of his dressing-gown pocket, aimed it full at the Magician's head, and the blow laid him flat on the floor.

The other pursuers now entered the shop. As soon as they had bound the Magician, their attention was directed to the Dummy in the Doctor's clothes, who lay there looking forlorn enough. Without the Doctor's broad, dignified hat, with only one eye and his face battered in, he certainly was not what he had appeared to be the night before.

How they all laughed over the shattered sham! The Doctor was for pulling it to pieces and burning it up at once. But the Mayor, who just then came in, said "No—Let us carry Monsieur Dummy into the public square, by broad daylight, and show the people of Toppledown, a second time, how they have been fooled."

The Magician was then carefully guarded and taken to prison to await his trial.

The legend declares that many great changes and improvements in the condition of Toppledown and of Fog-land, generally, date from this *denouement*, and that Doctor Theophilus was married late in life, but my friend, the original narrator, is disposed to accept the accounts that survive only with qualifications as History. Therefore I have considered it best to draw the curtain at this point—and leave the tale to be read in the light of whatever interior meaning may be discovered therein.

For the young, a magic-story.
For the old, an allegory.